THE STAMMERING

THE STAMMERING HANDBOOK

A definitive guide to coping with a stammer

Jenny Lewis

with The British Stammering Association

VERMILION
London

First published in the United Kingdom in 1997 by Vermilion
an imprint of Ebury Press
Random House
20 Vauxhall Bridge Road
London SW1V 2SA

Random House Australia (Pty) Limited
20 Alfred Street, Milsons Point, Sydney,
New South Wales 2061, Australia

Random House New Zealand Limited
18 Poland Road, Glenfield,
Auckland 10, New Zealand

Random House South Africa (Pty) Limited
Endulini, 5A Jubilee Road, Parktown 2193, South Africa

Random House UK Limited Reg. No. 954009

A CIP catalogue record for this book is available from the British Library

ISBN: 0 09 181660 2

Typeset in Monotype Century Old Style
Printed and bound in Great Britain by
Mackays of Chatham PLC, Chatham, Kent

CONTENTS

INTRODUCTION

Through speech we tell other people who we are, what we think and how we feel. Speech is an essential emotional outlet. When we are upset or depressed speaking to someone helps ease the hurt. When we are angry, expressing the anger often gets rid of it. Having a laugh with friends or even sharing a joke with a stranger can be immensely uplifting. When you have to think about every word you utter, or are anxious about other people's reactions to your lack of fluency, speaking can become a strain and a struggle and this essential form of self-expression is denied.

Stammering can profoundly affect every part of the person's life. A person who stammers is likely to have difficulty in saying his or her name and address, answering the telephone, ordering a meal, asking for a ticket and doing all the everyday things that require speech and that other people take for granted.

Most stammerers are aware that some people are impatient or uncomfortable waiting for them to get the words out. This, of course, adds pressure to the situation and makes the stammering worse. When people finish sentences for the person who stammers they can misconstrue what he or she is struggling to say and deliver the wrong message. This adds more pressure to an already stressful situation. For these reasons and others, many stammerers feel inhibited about joining in conversations in the normal way and taking part in a full social life.

Most people start stammering in childhood. By the time they have become adults they have experienced a lifetime of not saying things because it is difficult to do so. It is not surprising that many stammerers become withdrawn and isolated, sometimes believing themselves to be people who do not have ideas and opinions because their voices are so rarely heard. Many people who stammer feel that the rest of the world does not know who they are because they have not been given a chance to express themselves.

Yet people who have lived most of their lives not talking have usually spent a great deal of time listening. In so doing they may have gained an understanding of and sensitivity to people and situations at a much deeper level than a more fluent person may have done. The ability to listen and understand what is being said behind the words spoken is of immense value, both in social and in work situations. Socially, to talk to someone who actually listens is both reassuring and therapeutic. In the workplace, 'active listening' is an extremely valuable skill in many different areas, including such commonplace activities as negotiating, interviewing and planning.

Stammering is not just socially handicapping. In the workplace, verbal communication is now more important than it has ever been. Being able to talk on the telephone is part and parcel of many work situations. Being able to introduce yourself, talk about your company and your job, answer queries and speak to customers are everyday requirements in the workplace.

Many stammerers who are well qualified are refused employment on the grounds that they are not able to cope on the telephone, so they may be forced to take jobs that are well below their capability. Sometimes this downward spiral starts in childhood. Children who stammer often have problems at school. Some will drop out of formal education at the earliest opportunity, fail to obtain the qualifications they need and could get and fall far short of achieving their potential.

However, many people who stammer lead very full and successful lives, both socially and at work. Some will have stammered severely in childhood and as adults but have subsequently managed sufficiently to overcome the dysfluency to get on and succeed in whatever they want to do.

Aristotle, Isaac Newton and Winston Churchill were all stammerers, as were Lewis Carroll, Marilyn Monroe and Frankie Howerd. Currently there are many public figures who stammer in their private lives. A number of well-known actors, politicians and writers stammer and yet are pursuing highly successful careers. And, of course, there are many more stammerers who, although not famous, are achieving their career potential and living their social lives to the full.

The first step to overcoming the down side of anything is to acknowledge that it exists. This is true of stammering. The longer you continue to deny and disown the condition and the effect that it is having on your life, the longer you are putting off doing anything about it. And the longer you leave it, the more difficult it becomes to alter the situation.

If you are the parent of a child who stammers, Chapters Two and Three describe the many ways in which you can help your child gain increased fluency. If your child is under five years old, there is a good chance that, by taking it in hand now, you will be able to get rid of the stammer completely.

Some parents who consult their doctors or health visitors about their child's stammer are told to 'ignore it and it will go away'. Many young children do stumble over their words when learning to talk and then move on to normal speech, but there are some children who continue to find talking difficult. If you think your child is stammering, it is important to get help from a speech and language therapist as soon as possible.

In a child under the age of five, stammering therapy has a very high rate of success. It becomes more difficult as the child gets older. Adult stammerers can become much more fluent but the stammer is rarely eradicated altogether.

Parents of children who stammer sometimes do not appreciate all the implications of being a stammerer. This may be particularly the case when the child comes from a family where stammering is known. Perhaps Great Uncle Henry who stammered was well liked in the community in which the family lived and enjoyed a happy and successful life despite his dysfluency. But the world he inhabited has changed radically, and continues to change. The community and way of life he knew may have disappeared or altered beyond recognition. He may have done manual work that relied very little on speaking skills.

Today's four-year-olds who stammer are likely to have a much greater need of fluency as the working pattern in the world changes. They may also be living not in a community that knows them well, but in an environment where most people are strangers and it is important to talk in order to make friends.

Often it is in the teenage years that people first come to terms with the fact that their stammering is not going to go away but will probably be with them for the rest of their lives. The reality of this can be both shocking and depressing during this turbulent life stage. (Stammering in teenagers is discussed in Chapter Five.)

Adults who stammer can make enormous strides in improving their fluency, if this is what they want to do. Different people have different perceptions of how little or how severely they stammer and they also set themselves different goals for improvement. Some want to reduce their stammering to a point where the stammer is barely detectable. This can be achieved but sometimes the effect is to make the person sound more stilted and wooden.

Other people say that they want to stammer more smoothly. By this they mean that they accept the fact that they stammer and they want to control it, rather than eliminate it. This is also referred to as 'stammering more fluently'. The aim here is to retain the person's individual, characteristic pattern of speech but increase their fluency to the extent that their speech moves on from word to word and sentence to sentence. The idea is to remove the blocks and not worry about the stammer.

The best help available for stammering is speech therapy and this is discussed in Chapter Eight. However, there are a variety of techniques and self-help ideas that you can try for yourself. Some of these are outlined in Chapter Ten.

The incidence of psychological problems in stammerers is no greater than in the rest of the population. However, being a stammerer may well cause emotional problems. If you were constantly teased as a child and have experienced rejection because of your speech as an adult, you may believe that fate has dealt you a bad hand. You may feel resentful about not being able to fulfil your potential and angry that your needs are not being met and your voice is not being heard.

A good psychotherapist or a speech and language therapist trained in counselling can help you to talk about your feelings in a relaxed and non-judgemental way. He or she can help you express yourself and in so doing ease some of the hurt. As you gain a better image of yourself, you may find that you feel more confident and able to put into practice some of the techniques that will improve your speech. You may also find that you are less anxious about stammering and more able to take a chance and speak. Psychotherapy is explained in Chapter Nine and some of the different therapies that help you to learn to relax are outlined in Chapter Eleven.

Throughout this book you will find the personal stories of people who stammer. Many of the feelings and the incidents related may feel very familiar to you. You will see that, just as different people have different ways of stammering, methods of coping with the condition differ from person to person. Many of the people interviewed have found ways of dealing with their stammering so that it no longer hampers their lives. Maybe you can do the same. The stories do not necessarily link directly or only to the chapter in which they appear. Most of the people discuss how stammering affects various aspects of their lives.

Finally, although 80 per cent of people who stammer are men, many women stammer too. For this reason I have referred to stammerers as 'he or she' as much as possible and then reverted to 'he' for the sake of brevity.

1

WHAT IS STAMMERING?

'Stammering' and 'stuttering' are two different words that are used to describe the same condition. Generally speaking, 'stuttering' is used more commonly in North America and Australia, while in Britain we tend to say 'stammering'.

Stammering affects about 1 per cent of the population which constitutes about half a million people in the UK alone. Speech that is hesitant and jerky is often referred to as stammering. Stammering can make both the stammerer and the listener feel uncomfortable. Different people stammer in different ways. Some may repeat words or sounds or prolong them. Others may experience a partial or complete blockage or inability to say some words and sounds and this can involve the blocking of the airflow needed for speech. Some stammerers experience all these difficulties in speaking.

Many people who stammer find that trying to get the words out takes a lot of physical and mental effort. This struggle to speak can involve facial grimaces and other physical movements. Some people will speak fluently when they are on their own or talking to, for instance, a family pet. Other people will stammer in any situation.

The condition usually starts in early childhood. Very occasionally it can come on after a brain injury, for instance, as a result of a car crash, a stroke or any other similar illness. Stammering can be triggered by a traumatic event at any age. No one really knows what causes stammering but different theories abound. What is generally agreed is that there is no single cause for stammering but a combination of different factors is involved.

· Some Theories ·

One theory is that stammering is not so much a dysfunction of the person but a bad reaction to a normal phase that everyone goes through in childhood. When they start to speak, at the age of two or three, most children do not speak fluently. Their ability to express what is going on in their heads is limited. They tend to hesitate and repeat words.

There are some people who take the view that critical and over-anxious parents who want their child to perform may be putting their offspring under too much pressure. The child tries too hard to get it right the first time and struggles, which, it is suggested, could develop into stammering. However, there is no hard evidence to confirm this.

The current consensus view is that the child is born with a genetic predisposition to be less efficient at producing speech; if the parents are especially demanding towards the child, this might tip the balance. *However, it is generally accepted that even if a parent is very pushy and demanding, this will not in itself create a stammerer.*

Nearly 80 per cent of stammerers are male. The theory put forward to explain this is that male and female brains develop in different ways and at different times. The female brain develops earlier and therefore a little girl is more likely to cope with the function of co-ordinating speaking and thinking earlier on in life. A little boy may have more difficulty in early childhood because his brain has not yet acquired the capacity to deal with the complicated business of fluent speech. He may therefore speak dysfluently for longer than his female counterpart. If it becomes established that he has problems with speech the boy may go on to become a stammerer.

There was a time when children who wrote with their left hands were persuaded to change to their right. The idea may have been that everybody should be the same, and the majority of people were (and are) right-handed. Some incidents were reported of children starting to stammer at the point when they were asked to change from writing with their preferred hand, possibly because this adversely affected the hemisphere of the brain responsible for speech.

What normally happens is that, at the same time as the child establishes whether to be left- or right-handed, he is also establishing which half of his brain will dominate the process of speech production. In a right-handed person, it is usually the left hemisphere that dominates speech and the reverse is true for a left-handed person. It was thought that if you interfere with that process you confuse the brain in some way.

However, research has shown that there is no difference between stammerers and non-stammerers as regards the proportion of left- and right-handed people. Another problem lies in the fact that in an environment rigid enough to enforce right-handedness there may well be sufficient other pressures on a child's communication skills to tip him over into dysfluency. In *The Handbook on Stuttering*, published by Chapman and Hall, Oliver Bloodstein suggests that the theory that enforced right-handedness causes stammering is 'one of the curious superstitions of our time'.

There are also a lot of theories about the larynx. One is that the larynx of people who stammer has a tendency to 'seize up' much more easily than that of non-stammerers. One of the techniques used to control stammering is called 'passive airflow'. The person exhales a little before each word, thus preventing the larynx from seizing up.

Other people say that it is less to do with the larynx than with incorrect breathing. They believe that if stammerers are taught to breathe properly, through the diaphragm, they will get the full surge of breath required to complete the words.

Although no one has identified a gene that causes stammering, there is a strong belief in a genetic factor. There is a 20 per cent greater chance of a person stammering if he or she has a close relative who has a stammer.

These are some of the diverse theories on the causes of stammering. They all agree that no single factor leads to stammering; rather, it is caused by a number of different neurological, psychological and environmental factors.

· *Dealing with the Stammer* ·

According to The British Stammering Association, what tends to happen is that people recognise that they stammer and that it is a problem, but do nothing about it, hoping that the stammer will either disappear in time or that they will be able to get by in spite of it. Many stammerers become very skilful at appearing fluent, adopting elaborate strategies to avoid 'difficult' words or certain speaking situations. Others do little or nothing about their stammer until a crisis occurs that pushes them to take action. At this late stage, dealing with the stammer can be quite a major undertaking.

Everybody experiences a certain amount of dysfluency of speech. If you listen attentively to people who don't stammer you will notice plenty of 'ers' and 'ums' in their speech. They will repeat sounds and phrases. Some may mumble, swallow their words or not quite finish a sentence. Others may talk too softly or too loudly or speak very quickly, so that you have trouble keeping up with what they are saying. Not everyone who doesn't stammer is a joy to listen to. Very few people are able to articulate sentence after sentence in an entirely fluent way. Even in the non-stammering world verbal fluency varies enormously from person to person.

The same is true of stammering. Even somebody with a severe stammer will speak fluently at times, usually when they are relaxed and not under pressure. Many, if not most, stammerers will fluctuate in their fluency. They will have good days and bad days and there will be situations that promote fluency and those that inhibit it.

Given that everyone has variable fluency, perhaps the only real thing that separates the person who stammers from the one who does not may be the confidence to communicate verbally. If you are afraid to pick up the telephone, order a meal in a restaurant or engage in a conversation that will entail using a lot of words on which you become blocked, there will be a big gulf between you and the person who ums and ahs his way through life.

However, if you can get to the point where you are prepared to speak (albeit dysfluently) virtually at any time and on any occasion, nothing, in real terms, separates you from the normal speaker. Speech and language therapists, particularly those who specialise in stammering, can be of enormous help to children and adults who stammer in achieving this goal. If you have a child who stammers, it would be advisable to take him or her to a speech and language therapist. Some of the ways you can recognise that your child is a stammerer as opposed to one who is just going through a dysfluent period are discussed in Chapter Two.

Speech and language therapists are available privately and on the National Health Service, but the waiting time varies from area to area and so does the type of therapy. Some people prefer to try to help themselves and this can be very useful too.

The first thing you need to do is to turn the spotlight on your stammering instead of trying to forget about it. How do you stammer? Do you repeat sounds ('s-s-s-supper')? Or syllables ('su-su-su-supper')? Or do you prolong sounds ('sssssupper')? Do you get blocked in speech so that you cannot make any sound?

In the leaflet, 'The Adult who Stammers', The British Stammering Association says: 'Once you have begun to think about your stammer as being like a jigsaw puzzle, with small pieces that fit together and make up the whole, you can then tackle one piece at a time.'

Stammering isn't just a speech problem. There are people who have come away from intensive speech and language therapy courses with no marked improvement to their stammering, but an enormous change in their perception of it. Their former embarrassment about speaking has been replaced by confidence and a belief that they have a right to be heard; if people have to wait a little to hear them, so be it. Nothing much has altered in their speech; the shift has taken place in their heads.

It seems that there are two main components to stammering: the physical, which you can see and hear, and the emotional, which comprises all the issues and feelings that are part and parcel of stammering. The late Dr. Joseph Sheehan, who was a Professor of Psychology at the University of California, used an interesting metaphor to describe these two different components. He likened stammering to an iceberg: there is the bit that you see bobbing up above the surface of the water and the bit that you don't see because it is submerged.

Just as in the physical iceberg both parts are equally real and important, both components of the stammerer's iceberg are present, whether they are visible or not. Every stammerer has these two parts to his stammering, but what differs with each individual is the proportion of the iceberg that is visible to that which is hidden.

Take Harry, for instance, who is young and naturally outgoing and whose dysfluency has not held him back very much. The greater part of his iceberg is above the surface of the water. Harry's stammer is obvious. Everyone who meets him knows that he has a problem with speech, but Harry has not accumulated all the anxiety, hurt and feelings of unworthiness that can accompany stammering.

George, on the other hand, is an adult with a very different experience. He suffered teasing as a child and discrimination in the workplace and feels socially isolated. He never answers the telephone and rarely puts himself in situations where he has to speak. He talks very little in social gatherings, mainly smiling and nodding. He occasionally allows himself to say the odd sentence that incorporates all the avoidance tactics that he has learned over the years. People see George as someone who is more of a listener than a talker and assume that he is quite content to be so. They do not see the George who is dying to get out, the person inside who is longing to talk and argue and express himself just as his friends do. Very little of George's iceberg appears above the surface of the water. Even though George's speech may be more fluent than Harry's, his disability is the greater.

A captain in charge of a ship will have enormous respect for the bit of the oceanic iceberg that is hidden below sea-level because of the damage it can do. The stammerer's iceberg is not dissimilar. The part that is submerged can be very destructive if its existence is not acknowledged and catered for.

How do you picture your iceberg? How would you draw it? Since there are different ways in which you can tackle the problem of stammering, it may be useful to picture your own iceberg in order to identify what the real issue is for you. Is it above the water or below it? Is it mainly physical or are the emotional aspects more important to you? Here are Harry's and George's icebergs. Perhaps you would like to draw your own.

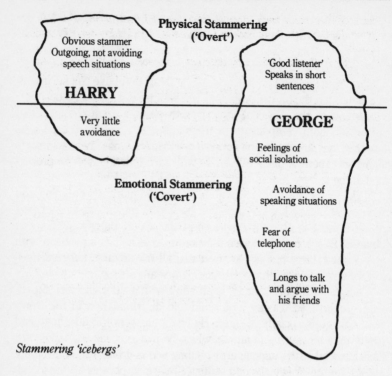

Physical Stammering ('Overt')

Obvious stammer
Outgoing, not avoiding
speech situations

HARRY

'Good listener'
Speaks in short
sentences

Very little
avoidance

GEORGE

Feelings of
social isolation

Emotional Stammering ('Covert')

Avoidance of
speaking situations

Fear of
telephone

Longs to talk
and argue with
his friends

Stammering 'icebergs'

· *John* ·

John started to stammer more or less when he started to speak, at the age of three. He believes that it was probably due to having a father who was short-tempered and impatient for him to speak. Today his stammer is still quite severe, particularly when he is speaking about himself. At other times he can talk quite fluently and he is particularly adept at one-liners. John is quick-witted and good at seeing the funny side of things. He and his friend are known in their crowd as a couple of comedians and a good, comic double-act. John is 40 years old.

> *I think a lot of my stammer is psychological. My father is very quick-tempered and often used to shout. He would be very snappy with me and say things like 'Come on, get it out.'*
>
> *I had speech therapy for the first time, I think, when I was three years old. I had more when I was eight and some when I was fourteen. It didn't help me because they were trying to get me to say the words, but it was stuck in my brain that I didn't want to speak very much at all.*
>
> *I don't think I wanted to speak because I didn't want to be like my dad. When he shouted I would see other people's reaction. I think that might*

have affected me. I know I can be stubborn. If I don't want to do anything, I won't. I think somewhere in my mind I decided I wasn't going to speak.

After I left school I felt a bit different to everyone else. It finally hit me that my speech was going to be a hindrance. And I started being quieter than I used to be. You know everyone at school, so it's different. After I left I felt more odd. I didn't know anyone else who stuttered. I didn't like pubs because I couldn't speak anyway. I felt left out. I hardly went out anywhere.

But I went to discos and I danced and that helped me. I enjoyed the dancing because I didn't have to worry, I could do what I wanted; just messing about dancing. And that brought me out of my shell.

I owned a small mobile disco which I ran with a friend for four years when I was 20 to 24 years old. But I couldn't say anything on the microphone. In my spare time I used to customise and drive a beach buggy which consumed my money but increased my practical skills. I have now started my final project, which is a V8-engined trike.

I have now realised that the reaction of people to my stutter is similar to my father's shouting and this is probably why I close my eyes when I block. I am fairly cautious all the time which I believe is due to a one-inch maythorn entering my eye when I was about three and a half years old. I find it very hard to totally relax.

I went on an intensive speech therapy course at the City Lit [The City Literary Institute] a couple of years ago. There were 12 of us in the group. It helped my speech a bit but it also got me thinking about what might have started my stammer in the first place.

The stammering has restricted me in the jobs I can do. Because I stammer I work very hard at doing the best I can. I never went to university after school because I felt I wouldn't get a job worthy of a degree because of my speech, so there was no point. But I went to college to do the motor vehicle technician's course.

I went back to study a few years ago and did a course in electronic software. I was hoping to get work in that field but it didn't happen. But I did get a better job and I am now working on vehicle electrical wiring. The course taught me to understand electronic circuits and I now know exactly what they do. It's made me more knowledgeable in my work.

I am married and my wife has two married daughters. I don't have any children. I don't really want any. I know it's unlikely, but I wouldn't want them to have the same speech problems as I have. Also, because of my stammer, I feel I wouldn't be able to help them when they start to grow up. I couldn't teach them the right things.

I wish I could tell jokes. I can only do one-liners and I always get a laugh. They come out quickly and fluently. I think it's because I don't have to think. They come out from off the top of my head. I don't worry beforehand about what people are going to think or say. I have a friend who is good at telling jokes and we have a brilliant time when we go out together. I can often pick up on what people are saying and add to it. It keeps the whole thing going and it's really good.

Since the course at the City Lit, I am better. I know the techniques but I can't always use them. It feels as if there is something in my brain that stops me speaking. I used to have a silent block which was terrible. My throat would become tight so that I couldn't breathe and my face would go red. My muscles would tighten and my body would become very tense. It took a lot of effort. But it's better now. I can breathe slightly into the word. At least something is coming out. I feel more relaxed inside and my body is less tense.

But I still can't say my name sometimes. I just get stuck on it. I always get stuck when I'm saying something about myself. It's really annoying because I can't say the things that I want to say. When the attention has gone from me I can speak much more quickly. But you find in life that you have to talk about yourself quite a lot, don't you?

· *Margaret* ·

I started stammering when I was about three or four years old. My mother told me that they had just decorated the Christmas tree and put the Christmas lights on. They brought me downstairs and when I saw the tree I screamed. I think I must have been frightened by the lights. Apparently I started stammering soon after that. It might have been the shock. No one else in the family stammered.

I didn't have much bullying or picking on in school except at one school. There was one particular person there who would pick on me and make the others do the same. So my mother changed my school.

I went to speech therapy when I was about 11 years old and had changed schools. It was in a children's hospital. What we had to do was to make models out of paper. We made animals and bridges and we had to blow the animals over the bridges. We didn't do much more than that.

It makes you quieter than you would have been because you're afraid to speak. You're afraid of embarrassing yourself. We never talked about stammering at home.

My confidence was always very low. My school reports always said 'lacks confidence' in everything except English. I liked writing, competitions and essays. I always read a great deal. I wanted to be a librarian but that meant staying on to do my O levels and my parents didn't want me to do that. I think money was tight. I was 15 when I left school. I went to a local college to learn shorthand and typing. It worried me silly. All through my life I've found it very difficult to learn new things because of my lack of confidence. I think it may have come from the stammering but it is very difficult to say which comes first.

I worked in a shop as a sales assistant. I loved it. I like company. I love being with other people. I was an only child, which I didn't like. I found it very lonely. A shop with a lot of people really suited me. It made me talk. They would send me to buy cheese rolls, custards and different things like that. When my mother sent me out she would write a note for the shops with a list of things that she wanted. The shop I worked in didn't do that and it forced me to speak. Liking the job and liking the company helped an awful lot. I was a lot happier.

My daughter-in-law once remarked that I ask a lot of questions. I think that's because I can talk in short sentences and questions tend to be short. It's when I have to speak sentence after sentence that it is really difficult. That's why working in a shop suits me. Asking questions and answering them are all short sentences. I still work in a shop.

Because stammering makes you quieter it stops people knowing the real you. It also stops you doing a lot of things that you might do. I've been on committees and different things like that. I remember once being a secretary for a branch of the Townswomen's Guild, which was fine. I could do all the telephoning. But one year I was going to have to read out the annual report so I just left.

Reading aloud is one of the worst things I can possibly do. It doesn't help me as it does a lot of people. It makes me more nervous. It's as if I am afraid of the fear. They say you should face your fears and overcome them, so I have sometimes tried to do it. I am a Church Missionary secretary and part of that job is addressing the ladies' group. They are a very small friendly group of ladies who meet once a year. They expected me to address them because the previous people had. I was very scared of doing it, but I wrote it all down. It was terrible. I read it all but my stammer was simply awful because I was so frightened. I said to myself, 'Never again.'

I have three children, aged 43, 34 and 28. The middle one stammered for a short while. He went into hospital with a fractured skull and when he came out he stammered for a few weeks. His son has also stammered for a short while and got over it. None of them had speech therapy.

My stammer is much worse when I am emotional. When my daughter went to live in Ipswich I missed her terribly. Most of my contact with her is on the telephone and I suddenly found the telephone difficult because I became so emotional. Speaking to her is very emotional because I am so fond of her.

When I left my husband I went through a bad depression. My stammer was much worse, so much so that my mother-in-law said that she'd never noticed that I stammered before. She had known me for 33 years but she didn't know I stammered. When the emotional problems got better so did my stammer. I think for me it's best forgotten. Most of the time I can forget about stammering. I just push it to one side and carry on regardless.

If I've seen a good film or television or read a particularly good book, I find it difficult to tell people about it. That's when they'll find out I've got a stammer. I think it's because I've got to say sentence after sentence after sentence. Also, if I get excited about something I stammer. It's an emotional thing as well as a speech defect with me.

The only way I can control my stammer when it is really bad is not to speak.

2

CHILDREN WHO STAMMER

One of the most significant events in family life occurs when a young child starts to speak. For parents it is the transition from caring for an infant who can communicate only by laughing, crying, pointing or other forms of body language to relating to someone who can speak. Some parents find the non-verbal stage of a child's life confusing and frustrating and are far more confident of meeting their offspring's needs once they can talk.

For young children learning to talk is very exciting. For the first time they can communicate with their family and friends. Being able to ask for what they want, albeit in a limited and uncoordinated way, gives a child a sense of self-sufficiency and power which helps him or her to gain a feeling of self-confidence.

However, learning to speak is not a simple process. It requires co-ordination of thought and words. The young child needs to learn which sounds we use in our language and how they are put together to form words. He then has to be able to find the words to express his thoughts. This may be difficult because he does not as yet have the vocabulary. To speak with a degree of fluency, the child has to put the words he knows in the right place in the sentence to get across what he is trying to say.

He also needs to be able to listen and understand what other people are saying. Young children live very much in the present and their feelings can be very intense. They have limited patience and acquiring these skills can be as frustrating as it is exciting.

In addition, children need to develop motor skills so that they can copy the sounds that other people use in order to be understood. They have to co-ordinate all the muscles used for breathing and speaking and to be able to control them sufficiently to move smoothly from one sound to the next.

You may find that there are times when your child speaks more fluently than at others. Perhaps he is much more coherent when he has just woken up in the morning or after his afternoon nap than in the evenings, when he is tired and crotchety. Just as even fluent-speaking adults can find it more difficult to be articulate when they are overtired or emotionally overwhelmed, young children's speech can deteriorate remarkably when they are ill, tired, over-excited or upset.

It can be very difficult for parents to know what to do with a young child who appears to be dysfluent. Should you simply hope that the child will naturally grow out of it, as the majority do? In some ways this option seems attractive because it does not focus on speech or make the child anxious about speaking. On the other hand, the earlier children receive help for stammering, the better are their chances of recovering. Many adult stammerers have said that they wished that the condition had been treated when they were very young. In this, as in many other situations, it can be hard for parents to win!

If you are worried that your child may be stammering, get professional advice. One parent of a child who stammered said that when her son was four years old she suspected that he might be dysfluent. Her doctor referred her to a speech and language therapist whom she and her son saw regularly. The meetings with the therapist were very low-key and relaxed. The child was not aware that he was receiving therapy and the mother was given suggestions on how she could help her young child to achieve greater fluency. Now, in his twenties, he does not stammer at all and is unaware that he ever did.

· *How Stammering Can Develop* ·

Between the ages of two and five it is quite common for children to speak jerkily and hesitantly with lots of 'ers' and 'ums' while they are learning to talk. About five in every hundred children struggle significantly more with their speech for a while, but for most of these this phase will pass as they become older. Other children go through months of being fluent, only to resume their dysfluency.

For those children who do not grow out of it, their dysfluent speech can happen so often that it interferes with talking or makes both the speaker and the listener feel uncomfortable. This pattern of speech is stammering. The child may become very tense and struggle to get the words out or finish a sentence.

There is no evidence that parents can cause a child to stammer. It is thought that some people may be born with a predisposition to it, but by and large no one really knows why people begin to stammer. The feeling is that there is no single cause for stammering, but that a combination of different factors is involved.

What parents can do, however, is to try to make the home and family environment stammering-friendly so that the child does not become anxious about his speech. The next chapter shows how parents can help their young stammerer.

· Detecting Stammering in Early · Childhood

The onset of stammering is usually between the ages of two and five. In this age group stammering often fluctuates between periods of fluency and dysfluency. The severity of the stammering will vary according to circumstances. For example, the child may stammer more when he or she is tired or ill. He may stammer more or less depending on what he wants to say. If he is trying to convey a complex message he is likely to stammer more than if he is saying something simple.

Bear in mind that there can be several dysfluent patches as the period of fluency increases. Parents often believe that if a child has experienced a period of speaking fluently, he or she cannot possibly be a stammerer. This is not the case. In this age group it is not uncommon for stammerers to go through weeks, if not months, of fluent speech and then suddenly start stammering again. If this happens it is an indication that the child may be stammering and will need help to progress to fluent speech.

Children under five years old who receive therapy for their stammer have a good chance of gaining normal fluency. As we have seen, the earlier the child receives professional help, the greater are his chances of recovery.

Before you can detect what makes a stammerer, you first have to know what constitutes stammering speech. Below are some pointers compiled by The British Stammering Association. Take these only as a rough guide. They are not intended to diagnose stammering, as some of these features also appear in the speech of children who go on to recover spontaneously.

- The child is putting extra effort into saying his words.
- His speech is tense and jerky.
- He cannot seem to get started and no sound comes out for several seconds. For example, '. . . Where is Daddy?'
- He is stretching sounds in a word. ('I want a sssssweet.')
- He is repeating parts of words several times. ('Mu-Mu-Mu-Mu-Mummy.')
- He stops what he is saying before he has finished the sentence.

The child will not necessarily display all the above signs, but if a few are observed consistently, this is an important indication of stammering.

Here are some other pointers to help identify a child who is more likely to develop a persistent stammer. Again, he or she will not necessarily display all these symptoms. The first symptom is a prerequisite and it will be accompanied by one or more of the others.

- The child speaks in a dysfluent way.
- There is a family history of stammering or speech problems.
- The child is struggling to get his words out.
- He is experiencing any other kind of difficulty in learning to talk.
- The child appears to be upset or frustrated by his talking.
- People listening to him feel uncomfortable or upset when he is speaking.
- He is in a dual-language situation and is stammering in his first language.
- The child's general behaviour is worrying.

Do remember that these are just pointers. None of them in themselves are sufficient to detect a child who is likely to develop a persistent stammer. If, having read these indications, you are worried about your child's speech, discuss the situation with a speech and language therapist.

· *Late Starters* ·

Sometimes stammering starts late. This is quite rare, but it can occasionally happen that a child is more or less fluent in early childhood and then suddenly starts stammering later on. James, whose personal account appears in this chapter, started stammering when he was seven years old.

It may be that the child always stammered slightly, but the dysfluency was so insignificant that it wasn't noticed. Then something happened to aggravate what was a mild condition. Sometimes a change of school can have this effect. The child may go from a primary school, where he feels safe because he has known most of the teachers and the children all his school life, to a big school with a great many pupils and teachers whom he doesn't know. The child may become very anxious about his environment and may stammer more. The problem may be greatly aggravated by reactions such as giggling or teasing.

In very rare cases, a stammer may appear after a traumatic incident like a car crash, bereavement or divorce. The likelihood of a fluent speaker becoming a stammerer as a result of such events is very unlikely. What is more usual is that a child who is already a stammerer will become worse as a result of a traumatic experience.

· *Talk About It* ·

Many adult stammerers have said that their stammering was not talked about when they were children. It can be difficult for anyone to speak about things that they know the other person finds difficult or painful. As parents, we try hard to protect our children from anything that we think might hurt them. But talking about the child's difficulty in speaking in the way you would talk about anything else makes it seem less extraordinary. If your child has a cold, a cough or chicken-pox, you would probably not think twice about mentioning it. If you can talk about his speech in the same casual way as you would about any other condition, you are likely to give your child the impression that stammering is just something that happens like anything else.

There is no reason why you cannot speak about talking being hard or difficult without labelling it as stammering. When a child is very young, it is very hard to be sure that the dysfluency is stammering, so it is a good idea to talk about his speech and to be open about it. However, since the problem may not be stammering, there is no need to label it as such.

· *Getting Help* ·

Early intervention is of the essence in preventing young children from developing a chronic problem. The people who are in the best position to advise parents are speech and language therapists who specialise in stammering. You can see them on the National Health Service and privately. The waiting time and type of therapy varies. The British Stammering Association (BSA) has a directory of qualified specialist speech and language therapists. If you would like to know if there is one in your area, contact the BSA (their address and telephone number appears in Useful Addresses at the back of this book).

With young children, the therapist will try to find ways in which the parents can help them become more fluent by making small changes in the way the family behaves at home. Helping a child to become more fluent is not the sole domain of the therapist. It is when parents and therapists work together co-operatively that the best help is offered to the child.

· *The Michael Palin Centre for* · *Stammering Children*

This centre for stammering children was developed by a charity, the Association for Research into Stammering in Childhood, in partnership with Camden and Islington Community Health Services NHS Trust. The centre was named after Michael Palin, who played the part of Ken, a stammerer in the film *A Fish Called Wanda*. Palin was able to draw on his experience of his father, who stammered, for this role.

The Centre offers specialist speech and language therapy to children who stammer and their families throughout the United Kingdom and is staffed by a team of specialist speech and language therapists. It has the greatest concentration of expertise in childhood stammering in this country, but many of the services it offers are also available from highly qualified specialist speech and language therapists working in NHS trusts in other parts of the UK.

Since the Centre opened in 1993, it has seen an increasing number of referrals of children of all ages. One of the underlying philosophies of the Centre is that children and their families should receive help as early as possible and, in fact, more and more very young children are attending for assessment and treatment. Children attend with both parents unless it is a one-parent family, in which case the principal carer will attend.

Children and young adults aged between two and eighteen can be referred to the Centre. Referrals can be made by the child's doctor or through their local speech and language therapist. The service is free, but children who are referred from outside the Camden and Islington Trust area are normally funded by their local Health Authority or GP fundholder through an extra-contractual referral. Information on the referral procedure can be obtained from the Centre.

The initial appointment comprises a full and detailed assessment of the child's problem within the context of the family. This session provides the family with a greater understanding of stammering and makes recommendations for therapy that is appropriate to the needs of the individual families. Older children and teenagers take an active part during this planning stage.

Naturally, treatment varies according to the age and particular needs of the child and his or her family. With pre-school children, interaction therapy with the parents is often recommended. After assessment, parents attend six one-hour sessions of therapy with their child. The aim of these sessions is to help the parents identify the things they do that are helpful when they are playing and talking with their child and also to make a few small changes that may assist the child in becoming more fluent. This may include speaking more slowly, using less complicated words, asking fewer questions or encouraging the child to take the lead in play.

During the first few weeks parents have the opportunity to discuss general parenting issues with the therapist. For example, parents may wish to discuss alternative ways of managing bedtimes or any of the other situations that commonly worry parents, such as temper tantrums.

After a break of six weeks, a review session is offered to assess rogress. In many cases this is all that is required. However, further sions will be planned as appropriate.

Here is a case study provided by The Michael Palin Centre for mering Children which shows how their methods work.

· *Robert* ·

When Robert was three and a half years old his parents brought him to the Stammering Centre for an assessment. He was a bright boy with an advanced vocabulary. His speech was fast but his mind raced faster. He would grind to a stop and be unable to produce a sound or he would prolong it. His father had a slight stammer and his paternal grandmother also stammered.

Robert's stammer began in nursery school. At first he had repeated words but now his stammer was so severe he could barely be understood.

Robert's younger sister was two years old and was walking and talking. She had a dominant and extroverted personality. A video made of the family together at the centre showed that the children competed for their parents' attention. They constantly interrupted one another. Robert's stammer was at its worst when he tried to break into the conversation. But there was a pay-off: his efforts frequently earned him both parents' attention.

After the initial assessment, six treatment sessions were scheduled. Meanwhile, Robert's parents each spent five minutes' 'talking time' with him five days a week.

The family speech was also altered slightly. They slowed down their fast way of talking with the aid of video feedback. They simplified their language so that Robert did not have to struggle to use a style that was too difficult for him. They also looked at how they behaved as a family.

Each child enjoyed time individually with each parent and learnt to take turns in family group conversations. Robert was now allowed special privileges for being the elder child. One of these was that he went to bed after his sister. This gave him the opportunity to have his parents' attention to himself without having to compete with his sister.

Within six weeks Robert was fluent and two years on this fluency has been maintained.

Older children may begin with interaction therapy but go on to learn how to control their fluency themselves. Therapists are concerned with helping to equip stammering children in the older age groups with the skills to meet the demands of the school curriculum.

In addition to the weekly sessions there are also two-week intensive courses available for older children and teenagers.

Although separate bodies, The Michael Palin Centre for Stammering Children and The British Stammering Association co-operate fully in their work. Both are dedicated to serving the needs of stammerers and their families.

The address and telephone number of The Michael Palin Centre for Stammering Children is given in the Useful Addresses section.

· *James* ·

James is eleven years old. He started stammering when he was about seven. He had been pretty well fluent before then. His stammer came on so gradually that the family did not notice it was happening. But there was a period of four months when James hardly spoke at all. All he would say was 'yes' and 'no' and the family could not communicate with him at all. They found it heart-breaking. He attended two intensive speech therapy courses and he started to improve slightly. Then the family joined The British Stammering Association and James read aloud in front of 140 people at one of their conferences. He has subsequently given interviews to the press and has appeared on radio and television. All this has given him a lot of confidence despite the fact that he still stammers.

Trevor, James's father, says:

He has got a good attitude towards it, and this is something I have tried to impress on him. I've told him that he has to control his stammer himself. And if people look up at the ceiling when he's speaking, it's their problem and not his.

It was difficult when the stammering was first diagnosed. We did all the wrong things because we didn't know what to do. We tried to finish his sentences and tried to get him to slow down. Half the time it is because you feel uncomfortable yourself and, of course, you feel for him, especially when you go out and are in strange company. But now, as far as I am concerned, stammering is just part of James's character.

We have never really protected him. If he wants to buy sweets we've always sent him off to buy them himself. Over-protecting is a mistake a lot of people make. It's easy to let the child hide behind a stammer. As parents you want to protect your child but it's not helpful. We encourage James to do things. He does everything for himself now and we're quite relaxed about it.

Alison, his mother, has also made a point of going into James's school and talking to the teachers. They discuss what to do and what not to do. Sometimes a teacher will say that James has been naughty but she daren't tell him off because he stammers. Trevor and Alison insist that James is treated like any other child: 'If he misbehaves he must be told off in the normal way. You can't let him use the stammer to get away with things. We don't let him get away with using his stammer as an excuse at home.'

Here is James's side of the story.

I can't really remember what it was like when I started stammering but I imagine it was really hard to do things. I stammer more when it is getting near to Christmas or when I go on holiday or on my birthday. I want to say things but the words don't come out. It's a block. I've got the words in my mind but I can't actually bring them out. I don't know why that is.

People used to finish words off for me and I never liked that. They didn't give me time to say it and that's horrible. You feel you can't really say anything because nobody's giving you time. You feel you're not taking part in things. Also they sometimes finish it off with the wrong word and that's horrible too. For instance, I want to say 'I'm going down to the shop' and I say 'I'm going down to –' and I get stuck. If someone says 'You're going down to the video shop,' that's horrible. You think, 'No, I'm not. Why did they say that?' You have to work twice as hard to say what you actually meant to say after they've finished off the word. It doesn't help at all, really.

They don't do it so much now. I used to try to explain to them why they should stop finishing off the word for me. It makes it more difficult. It gives me more trouble than I can handle.

In my last school some big kids picked on me because I stammered. They thought, 'He's got a problem that shows so let's go and pick on him'. They would repeat words that I said, pretending to stammer. They started calling me horrible names like 'Stuttermouth'. I sometimes used to wish I was fluent. Everyday they would call me names. You would really want to hit them but you couldn't because you'd get into trouble. And if you hurt them you were going to be in big trouble.

I've never hit anyone. It isn't my style, really. But I've wanted to. It is hard to fight back. You can't fight back with talking because it's difficult and you can't hit anyone. It's horrible. It put me off school for a bit.

I liked school for lessons. I used to go to the teachers and ask them why the children were calling me names. The teachers would say they would sort them out but they would still do it the next day. Going to some teachers didn't achieve anything. It made me feel let down.

But some teachers really did understand and would sort the kids out. Others would just tell them to stop it. If they just said 'Stop it,' nothing would happen. They'd just keep on doing it.

When I was in the fifth year I had a really, really good teacher and she explained everything to the whole class. I was very pleased about that. It made everyone understand what people were going through, including me. It isn't nice to be bullied if you're fat, have a funny name or stammer. She explained to the other children what stammering was and that helped.

I used to really worry about reading aloud in class and answering the register but I don't worry about it now. Sometimes I struggle to get the first word out and it doesn't come for ages, but then it does and I'm fluent after that. People wait for me to get the word out and I don't get anxious.

3

How Parents Can Help

Parents of children who stammer are generally very supportive and caring towards them. Understandably, they may also be so anxious to help them overcome their difficulties that they try all sorts of different things, often without much success.

Children, like adults, differ in how they stammer, why they stammer and how they can overcome the problem. This chapter looks at some of the ways in which parents can help, if and when this is appropriate. Stammering is not always a family issue.

Speech and language therapist Rosemarie Hayhow says:

If I felt that the parents' behaviour was precipitating stammering I would work on parent interaction but it often isn't. It all depends where you think the stammering originates. It may be a problem that the child has within their system that they have got to learn to deal with. Or it may be a problem that exists within the family that the family has to learn to deal with.

Therapists must be clear about the hypothesis they are making concerning the nature of the problem that the child is experiencing and make sure that the therapy offered is addressing that particular hypothesis.

Much of the advice given in the following pages is aimed at removing some of the pressures on the child in relation to speech. The idea is to establish a more relaxed environment while the child is overcoming the difficulties and developing improved speaking skills. If you find that, when some of these suggestions are adopted, your child's fluency improves and the improvement is maintained over several months, you can assume that the plan is working. But if there is little or no change or the improvement is not maintained, don't despair. It doesn't mean that your child cannot be helped. It just means that he or she needs to be helped in a different way.

Willie Botterill, speech and language therapist at The Michael Palin Centre for Stammering Children, says:

Many parents come to therapy extremely distressed and often feeling guilty about their child, who had been speaking fluently but has become increasingly dysfluent despite their best efforts to help. They feel increasingly anxious as it doesn't seem to matter what they do; it just gets worse. Therapy is designed to help them to find things they can do that do help. When they know what to do it can help put them back in charge again.

Unfortunately, however, there is no set of rules which, if adhered to, will make everything all right. In addition to reading books, magazine articles or leaflets to gather information and to get ideas that they might try, they should also listen to their own instincts. If it works, that's great, but it is important to remember that each child and family are unique. What works for one family may be very different from another, which is why the advice can seem confusing and at times contradictory.

With those caveats in mind, let's look at some of the things you can do that may help your child. Some of the suggestions will be more difficult to put into practice than others. Do what you can as well as you can and leave it at that. Don't set yourself a goal that you cannot achieve. If it is too difficult and you fail, you may feel discouraged and upset. Neither you nor your child needs that. Bear in mind that you will not be able to change from being one kind of a family into a completely different one. Nor is this necessary. It would not feel natural and it wouldn't work. A little appropriate adjustment is all that is required.

· *Observe Your Youngster* ·

Try to make a conscious effort to find out in what situations your child stammers more. Keeping a diary or jotting down observations in a notebook for a few weeks might help you to get a picture of the stammering. Does he stammer more when he's excited, distressed, tired or worried? What happens in group activities? Does he stammer more or not speak at all? Does he stammer particularly badly when he is supposed to be on his best behaviour?

Do certain individuals increase the stammer? Some people are sticklers for manners and discipline. While it is nice to have well-mannered children, it is also important to strike the right balance. Try to bear in mind that, as the parent of your child, you are likely to be in a better position to know what that balance is. Outsiders may not be aware of all the implications.

'Pleases' and 'thank yous' can be enormously important to some people. Of course, it is nice to hear them from a fluent child, but such niceties may be too much to ask of a child who is experiencing difficulty with speech. It may be best to devise a way round them. Maybe you can encourage your child to smile when, for instance, he or she is given a present and leave it at that. Out of earshot of your child, tell your friend that at the moment the smile is a substitute for the pleases and thank yous and explain why. When your child has become more fluent or more confident in his speech, you could start encouraging him to say the requisite words.

Some visitors may want to engage your child in conversation, but if you know, through your observations, that this puts him on edge, try to forestall it as best you can. Strike up a conversation with your friend, or suggest your child watches television, for example. Do whatever seems most natural and appropriate. You may need to think about this beforehand. Don't make your child 'perform' for anyone, no matter how eminent, worthy or nice, unless he or she wants to.

It can sometimes be difficult with particularly dominant friends or relations to stay in control of any situation, including those that involve our children. However, it is important to try to do this, with children in general and the more vulnerable ones in particular.

· *Give Your Time* ·

One of the most important things you can do is to give your child some special time. About three times a week, set aside between five and ten minutes to spend with him or her. You can play games, do puzzles or talk. Take your cue from your child. Do what he wants to do, but make sure that he has centre stage and that he does not have to compete for your time and attention with others. If you have more than one child, you may want to include them in this arrangement, even if they are fluent. This avoids singling out the child who stammers and the build-up of resentment between siblings.

When your child wants to speak, give him plenty of time to finish what he is saying without interrupting. Look at him while he is speaking. This will reassure him that he has your full attention. He will also know that you are not embarrassed by his struggle to speak. Remember to keep things as relaxed as possible.

If you sense that your child is not sure that you have fully understood what he has said, there is no harm in reflecting it back to him once he has finished speaking. You don't have to repeat it word for word, so long as the meaning is the same. For instance, if you think he said: 'Can I stay up late tonight?' you can say: 'So you want to stay up late tonight. All right, you can have an extra ten minutes/No, I'm afraid you can't.' The important point is not to answer the question with another question, but to ensure that your child knows that he has been heard and understood.

From time to time you may find it helpful to reflect back what your child has said. If you don't overdo it, this is a useful way of letting him know that you understand what he is saying. Conversely, if you have got it wrong, let your child repeat what he has said. Wait patiently for him to reiterate. Don't rush him and don't finish the words or sentences for him; you may get it wrong again. Furthermore it is very important to get across to your child that he is fully entitled to say what he wants to say and to be understood. If it takes longer than normal, so be it.

Giving your child your attention at other times is also very important. Obviously, there will be many times when you are busy and you cannot stop and listen attentively. When this happens, you can do one of two things: you can explain to him that you are listening but you cannot concentrate hard on what he is saying at the moment but that you will give him your full attention later. Don't forget to keep your promise! It may be better to ask him to wait until you've finished what you are doing and then give him individual attention. It can be very frustrating to talk to someone who is only half-listening; waiting until you have time to listen properly remedies this.

· *Praise Your Child* ·

Remember to praise your child for the things that he or she is good at. We all need to be reminded from time to time of the things that we do well. Any child, whether he stammers or not, needs this too. Maybe your child who stammers draws nicely or is good at getting himself dressed. Whatever it is, find ways to boost his self-confidence, but make sure that the praise is genuine. Your youngster will know if you are being insincere and you will risk losing his trust. Find qualities or skills that you genuinely like or admire in him and focus on those. Of course, many parents do this already.

Willie Botterill agrees:

I think praise is very important. It is usually most effective if given to a child in context. For instance, when he comes in from outside and takes off his muddy shoes, praising him for remembering to do that without being asked and telling him that you thought it was a very responsible thing to do is good because it directly relates the praise to the activity. It also ascribes a characteristic – in this case, 'responsible' – which the child can begin to attribute to himself.

· *Don't Interrupt* ·

Try not to interrupt his or her speech. What he is saying may be incoherent or he may be prattling on; if he were any other child you might be tempted to tell him to start again. Don't do this with your child who stammers. Stammering is usually worse at the start of the speech. If you let him carry on speaking without interruption the stammering may well improve as he relaxes and gets into the flow. Each time you interrupt him and he has to start again, he is having to do the bit he finds hardest. This makes speaking a strain and a struggle with very little pay-off. He will have gone through the stress of trying to get the words out properly again and again. He may never achieve this and at the end of it all he will not have been allowed to say what he wanted to say. He may be discouraged from joining in conversations in the normal way. In addition, the interruptions may reinforce his difficulties with speaking and increase his stammer.

Another reason for not interrupting your child stammerer is that it negates what he has to say. If you keep interrupting with statements of your own, he may get the impression that you don't find what he is saying interesting or important. This will not encourage him to contribute.

Again, however, you have to try to get the balance right. If your child who stammers is reticent about speaking, the above suggestions may be helpful. But there are some dysfluent children who speak non-stop and they need to be encouraged to learn to give others a turn to speak without interruption.

It is quite a difficult balancing act, but it is important to try to avoid making your child who stammers a special case. As well as giving him or her the confidence to speak, you need to ensure that he has the social skills to interact with the world at large. He has to learn to take turns with others. His speech should not be interrupted; similarly, he needs to be able to give other people space to speak.

· *Don't Correct Speech* ·

Try not to correct your child's speech. Telling him or her to take a deep breath and start again is not helpful. But things like 'Calm down' or 'Take your time' can sometimes be effective if said calmly and gently.

It helps dysfluent children if their parents use simple language and speak slowly with lots of pauses. The child is likely to imitate this more relaxed way of speaking. It is extremely difficult to slow down speech when you have spent your life talking quickly. But if you can manage to slow it down a little, it can pay dividends. Also, try to keep your sentences short and simple.

Reduce the number of questions you ask. Questions invite answers, which means that your child is required to speak. Encouraging speech is one thing, demanding it is another. Just as you may have to ease off on the 'pleases' and 'thank yous', you may need to rethink your conversations with your stammering child in order to avoid putting him in a situation where he has to speak. Obviously, you can't avoid questions altogether and there is no reason to do this.

Wherever possible, try to restructure questions into statements. For example, 'Shall we go out for a walk?' could become 'Let's go out for a walk.' You cannot always do this, but when you do ask questions, keep them simple. 'What did you do at school today?' is a question that requires a complex answer. The child has to think about all the different things he or she did and construct an answer. Most children, whether they stammer or not, will answer that question with 'Nothing'! If you say, for instance: 'Did you have a good day at school today?' your child can nod or shake his head, or answer with a simple 'Yes' or 'No'.

If you follow this a few minutes later with: 'Did you paint?' again he can give a simple answer. The important thing is to allow him to reply before introducing another question. Give the child time to think. For instance you may have asked: 'Did you draw?' He may have nodded his head. Then perhaps the image of the big house that he drew may have come into his mind. He wants to tell you about it. If you've gone racing on to ask several other questions, he will not be able to do this. If, instead, you give him plenty of time, he may say: 'I drew a house.' And follow this up with: 'Our house'. This creates a coherent and informative dialogue.

Children who stammer generally prefer a calm and unhurried lifestyle. They tend to find a chaotic household where there is a constant flow of people and a lot of excitement very confusing. They cannot compete, because this usually entails speaking quickly. Also, they may have no opportunity to speak at their own pace and be listened to. Like any other child, the youngster who stammers will find a daily routine helpful if it is applied sensibly. It gives him a structure where he fits in and knows what is required of him. This provides a feeling of safety which can be beneficial when it comes to reducing stress in speaking situations.

Parents often notice that their child is more dysfluent when he or she is tired. Therefore, a regular bedtime which allows them plenty of time to get the amount of sleep they require will be important for some children who stammer.

· *Control the Competition* ·

Competing for attention in the family is a big problem for a stammering child. If you read Robin's story in Chapter Six, you will see that he cites as one of the factors that may have contributed to his stammer the fact that his mother and aunt talked incessantly and he 'couldn't get a word in edgeways'.

Imagine yourself in the following situation. You are with a group of people who are talking a foreign language. You understand the language fairly well, but you find speaking it much more difficult. This is a very common experience among people learning a new language. They will often say: 'I can understand most of what is being said but I don't really speak it very well.'

There you are, listening to what is going on. You are pleased with yourself for being able to understand what is being said; you want to show your friends that you have understood the conversation and you would like to join in. This is not easy. You have to find the words, put them in the right context in the sentence and then pluck up the courage to say them, hoping that you get the pronunciation right.

If your friends speak with plenty of pauses and refer to you every now and again, giving you a chance to say something, you probably will. You will speak and they will respond. If you have conveyed your message well enough for them to understand it, you will almost certainly feel a sense of satisfaction. You have communicated in a foreign language. You weren't sure that you could do it, but you did. The experience will undoubtedly give you the confidence to try again. As you chalk up more and more positive experiences of speaking the new language you will become increasingly confident, until one day you will be able to say: 'I speak the language.'

If, on the other hand, your friends jabber on, perhaps occasionally smiling at you but never giving you the chance to join in, you may feel discouraged and inadequate in your language skills. Your belief that you can understand but not speak will be reinforced.

The situation is not very different for a child who is starting to speak. The chances are that he or she will understand a great deal of what is being said. He will almost certainly want to join in, but it is not yet second nature for him to think of something and just say it. He needs time to work out the process.

In a large and expressive family, this may be difficult. When everybody has something to say the chances are that several people will often start to speak at once. In an adult situation, one person will stop speaking in order to give another a chance to reply. This is a courtesy that is rarely practised amongst children. If two children start to speak simultaneously, the most fluent speaker is the one who is likely to continue. If this keeps happening, the less fluent child may become more and more diffident about his ability to speak.

It is difficult to change the family dynamics in any major way and in the case of a lively, expressive family there is no reason why one should. It can be a very warm and stimulating environment to grow up in. What you can try, however, is to modify certain areas just a little.

You may need to observe what happens within the family. If everyone is speaking at the same time and it is sometimes difficult to get a word in edgeways, it may be that the parents need to teach all the children about taking turns. Do it gently and good-humouredly; if you can make a game out of it until it becomes automatic, so much the better.

You may find, for instance, that when the children come out of school they all want to speak at once. They all want to tell you what happened. Try to make sure that they take it in turns to be first. Children have a strong sense of what's fair and once this pattern of communication is established, it should make life much easier all round.

There are no hard and fast rules in all of this. What is important is that you are sensitive to your child's individual needs and try as best you can to respond to them.

· *Grammar and Pronunciation* ·

In due course your child will learn to speak reasonably grammatically, taking into consideration various colloquialisms. Equally, he will eventually pronounce words according to the local dialect. As we have said, starting to speak is a complicated process. The learner-speaker needs to be allowed to say what he has to say without worrying about grammar and pronunciation, certainly in the early stages.

Constantly to correct any young child who is starting to speak is inadvisable. To be picked up continually on grammar and pronunciation can be very inhibiting and handicapping.

Willie Botterill explains:

> Children in the early stages of stammering do enjoy talking and are not too bothered about it, but they do need to hear a corrected version of their speech if they are to move forward with it. It is not necessary to correct them, but very helpful to repeat what they have said, putting in the correction. So, for example, if the child says 'Tat's in the bot,' the parent can say 'Yes, the cat's in the box.' This makes no demands on the child, but supplies a correct model for him.

If the speech is so unclear that you are not sure what your child is saying, there is no harm in checking it with him. He needs to be understood and to know that he is understood. You can say something like: 'Did you say you wanted to watch telly?' Don't say: 'Now, start again and say it properly this time.' He is doing the best he can. And notice the use of the easy word: 'Telly', not 'Television'. Keep it simple.

· *Simple Speech* ·

It is very difficult to alter the way you speak, especially as an adult. However, here is an aspect that you may like to think about. To some extent, children copy the way their parents speak. If you use long words and complicated sentences, your child may try to do the same. He or she will naturally assume that that is the way to speak. But it is much more difficult to use long words and intricate sentences, of course. A child who speaks normally will in all probability cope with the extra burden on his speech-learning skills. A dysfluent child may not. If you have a child who stammers, try to use shorter words and simple sentences. He or she will find it easier to follow.

· *Discipline* ·

In any household, it is hard to strike the balance between instigating the right amount of discipline and becoming either too rigid or overpermissive. It is perhaps a little more difficult with a child who stammers. There are several criteria. You need to create an environment in which the child feels loved and relaxed and reasonably free to express himself without worrying about upsetting people or doing the wrong thing.

However, he or she needs to know what is right and what is wrong, what is permissible and what isn't. After all, whether or not he stammers, he is living in society and needs to know the rules. Furthermore, we all need boundaries. Place them too close and tight, and people feel restricted and trapped. Make them unclear and ever-changing, and they feel insecure. We need to know where we stand.

This is as much the case for a child who stammers as for any other child. As parents, we are concerned about all our children and can often become very anxious about the ones who are particularly vulnerable, but it is advisable to keep an eye on parity. Although you may feel especially anxious about your child who stammers, try not to allow it to become the dominating factor of family life. Don't make him or her a special case.

Children like to feel that they are the same as everybody else. If they believe that they are different, they become very anxious. Also, if you generally make one law for your child who stammers and another for the others, his siblings may very well resent him and he could feel quite isolated. If you make it quite clear that he is treated differently only where speaking is involved – and then only in some circumstances – the others should not feel so resentful.

We all need guidelines and rules to live by and your stammering child is no exception. Vague rules, grey areas and inconsistent discipline will leave your child feeling unsure of himself and insecure. This may make him stammer more. Keep the guidelines clear and the discipline as consistent as you possibly can without being rigid.

· *Sue* ·

Sue's son, Lawson, started stammering from the age of about two. He is now 11 years old and much more confident but, as she says in the account below, it has been a struggle. She has three other children and over the years she has learnt how to handle a child who stammers in the context of the family. You may find her experiences both interesting and helpful.

Lawson never spoke properly at all. I have an older boy and I was told that when children start to speak they have problems with certain words, but as time went on it got progressively worse and a lot of the time he would not speak at all. It was more a case of a point and a grunt. I contacted the health visitor when he was about four to see if anything could be done. We went to a speech therapist, who told me not to fill in words for him and to give him time to speak. She seemed to think that it would get better. It didn't at all, it just got worse. He was stammering over every letter of the alphabet. It was torture for him to speak.

I felt annoyed that nobody seemed to want to do anything at the time. They all thought it would go away, but it didn't. I was very upset for him. I realised that if we didn't do something soon he could have quite a horrendous life. We were put in touch with a local speech and language therapist who was absolutely tremendous. She has been with Lawson since very early on. I don't know what she does but she manages to calm him down. He is not as dysfluent as he used to be. He is 11 now and it has been a battle for several years.

I used to find it difficult to stop myself from finishing his sentences. If I didn't catch what he said I couldn't keep on asking him to repeat himself. A lot of the time I would just agree with him, hoping I had got it right!

I've learnt a lot over the years. I've had to be patient. You have to give them a lot of time. They hate being rushed or put under pressure, so I make my other children wait for Lawson to finish speaking. They have been fine with that. They are very protective of him, even the youngest one is. He has two brothers and a sister. If Lawson starts to say something and they chip in I tell them to wait. Or Lawson will say: 'I started first.' Normally they now know to wait until he has finished. If he chips in when they are saying something, I ask him to wait his turn. He is not treated any differently because of his stammer.

If he does something wrong he is still punished. I used to see to him first, but I was told that that was where I was making a mistake. It made him stand out and seem different. If I carried on doing that, it would make him think that everyone would stop and listen to him when he started to speak and that isn't the case.

Lawson had a few problems at school. The other children would pick on him. I went to the school to get it sorted out, but the teachers seemed to be of the opinion that Lawson was using his stammer to get out of doing things he didn't want to do. If he didn't want to do something he would stammer. They thought he was putting it on but I knew he wasn't. I explained that his stammer needed to be handled carefully. They didn't seem to know how to handle him properly.

At primary school there was a question of whether Lawson was suitable for mainstream education. They put him in a special educational needs class. It meant he got extra help and one-to-one teaching, but it didn't help with his confidence. Where other children were concerned the bullying increased. Singling him out in the special needs class meant that he stood out even more. People thought that because he couldn't speak properly there was something wrong up top. He is a remarkably bright child. He ran rings around the educational psychologist who was brought in because the teachers thought that something else might be wrong with him. There was nothing else wrong with him.

He has now made his own group of friends and he gets on very well with them. I notice that when he is with them he doesn't seem to stammer quite so much. It doesn't disappear totally, but it improves and the longer he plays with them the better it gets.

Lawson still stammers over certain words. If he worries over something or gets really excited, he is terrible and it can be a real problem understanding what he is saying. We have to calm him down and let him do his relaxation exercises and start again. That helps because it brings him under control and he manages to get his words out.

He still has reservations at school, but it is not so bad because they don't make him wait. If he has to speak in the class, he tends to be the first. He doesn't have to wait in a queue and get worked up. The junior school hadn't a clue about how to handle the situation and the teachers didn't know how to cope either. Apparently they had never had a child who stammers in their class or school before. I couldn't believe that. The others may just have been camouflaging it. I told them that they had to find out as much as they could about stammering and that I would help.

I received leaflets from The British Stammering Association and sent them to the school. In the junior school there was only one teacher who took time to read them and that was mainly because he was a stammerer himself.

I think that if the government could give teachers more information while they are in teacher training college, it would go a long way to helping to overcome these problems because they would be better informed.

Now at school the teachers give Lawson time to speak and they maintain eye contact. They have also clamped down quite a bit on the teasing.

To other parents I would say: 'Don't tread on eggshells where your child is concerned. Treat him as a normal child because he is normal. There is nothing wrong with him. Parents have to accept the fact that their child has a stammer. It is no good sweeping it under the carpet and hoping it will get better. It won't. It cannot be cured but people who stammer can be taught how to control it.

It took me a little while to accept it and the guilt was incredible. I felt it was all my fault. I felt I had let him down and that maybe it was the way I had taught him to speak. Even now I have occasional guilt trips or think, Why me, why my son?

Give your child lots of encouragement and praise, because it is a question of self-esteem a lot of the time. Really define the praise; boost it up; be sincere; never fob them off. If they are having trouble at school, don't let it slide – talk to the school. Get your speech and language therapist involved with the school and liaise with everyone. It makes the child's life a lot easier. A lot of children don't want their teachers to know that they stammer, but it is of the utmost importance that they do know. Go in and speak to the class teacher or headteacher. If you haven't got a speech therapist, pester the health visitor or your doctor. Demand your rights! You'll probably find that there is quite a long waiting-list, but be patient and keep going back and reminding people. Basically, build up your child's confidence, stamp on bullying and be patient.

4

SCHOOL-DAYS

Research has shown that, at any given time, a little over one per cent of children attending school stammer. In a school with a roll of a thousand that means that there are likely to be at least ten pupils who stammer. For many of these children, school can be a misery. They may have to put up with merciless bullying from their peer group. They may encounter teachers who do not understand their problems and, even if they are caring and sensitive to their needs, their teachers may not know how to help.

Children who stammer may find themselves heavily disadvantaged when oral skills are required. For many, reading aloud can be a nightmare. Answering questions in front of the class is another persistent hurdle that the stammerer has to jump. He or she may know the answer, but getting it out quickly in front of an impatient teacher and sniggering classmates can be an impossible task. Calling out their name in the register can be traumatic for some stammerers.

However, some of these problems can be overcome with information and education. Often the teacher who seems impatient simply does not know how to handle a child who stammers. He or she may feel clumsy and inadequate when dealing with the stammering and project some of these feelings on to the young person.

Take this scenario: Anne, the teacher, feels uncomfortable in the presence of George, who stammers, because she does not know how to react to him. In one-to-one sessions with George she is more relaxed, but in front of the class she finds it hard to cope. She feels the spotlight is on her. George holds up the class in reading and answering questions. He does not seem to be able to get the words out. In the meantime, his classmates are getting restless, fidgety and perhaps misbehaving. Discipline is becoming an issue. Anne feels under pressure to maintain control and her dignity. She may have problems with this anyway. She feels angry and inadequate and, since she does not want to blame herself she blames George. Why can't he pull his socks up and speak like anybody else?

You may feel irritated with Anne, but most of us feel angry with people who shine a torch on our inadequacies, even though we may know that it is not their intention. Anne is just acting instinctively. What she needs is information on the best ways to handle a child who stammers.

Sometimes teachers who do not know how to cope with stammering adopt the trial-and-error method. They may feel that if they try hard enough they will eventually get there. Sadly, although this may be caring, it is not always helpful. Some of the 'trials' may be damaging. Finishing the sentence for the child who stammers, for instance, may make the teacher feel better because the embarrassment time is shortened and controlled.

The teacher may also believe that he or she has contained the discomfort for the child. But she may also have inadvertently given the child the message that stammering is embarrassing, not allowed or time-wasting. Furthermore, she has denied the child the opportunity to express himself. She may also, of course, have misconstrued what the child was going to say and have finished off the sentence incorrectly.

Some teachers may give the child special attention. This, too, can have its down side. No child wants to be a special case. It makes him feel different. Making an appointment to see a child in private, perhaps to talk about stammering, is one thing; continually to single him out for special attention or praise is another.

Parents often feel very diffident about approaching teachers. They are, after all, figures of authority. The word 'teacher' may be linked in our minds with the teachers we remember from our own school-days, when they were large and seemingly powerful and we were small and vulnerable. As parents, we have to remember that we and our children's teachers are all adults and the relationship is a more equal one.

Getting things right at school is extremely important for the child who stammers, and it is not just a question of education. Many adult stammerers say that they do not go for interviews for jobs they know they can do because they do not believe they will be offered the job. Others are in work that is far below their capabilities and are bored rigid. There is no reason why any person who stammers should not apply for – and get – a job that will give them satisfaction. All they need is the belief that they can succeed, and school is the best place to foster that belief.

If, as a schoolchild, you experience a positive attitude from your teachers and friends, you will carry that feeling of self-worth into your adult life. Eleven-year-old James, whose story closes Chapter Two, has a very positive view of what the world has to offer him, despite having a fairly severe stammer.

Your child needs to grow up expecting to do all the things the other children do. If he has an opinion which he wants to express in front of the entire class, he should be able to do just that without fear of being ridiculed, interrupted, hurried or having his words said for him. He should expect people to wait for him to say what he has to say in his own time, because he should feel that what he has to say is of value.

You can instil this attitude into your child by following some of the guidelines suggested in the previous chapters. But you also need the co-operation of your child's teachers. Being accepted as a valued member of his peer group is extremely important to the emotional well-being of your child. His or her teachers can help in this, but they have to be motivated and they have to be clear about what they are doing. When James's teachers just told the bullies to 'Stop it,' nothing happened. However, the 'really, really good teacher' did a bit more than that; she helped change the world for James.

The British Stammering Association has launched a project to advise and inform schoolteachers and the education authorities about ways to help schoolchildren who stammer. An initial part of the project was a series of seminars organised on different aspects of the problem. A big component of the seminars was work done in discussion groups by young stammerers themselves, who not only identified the main problems they faced at school but also suggested ways in which these problems could be solved. Teachers, parents and speech and language therapists as well as adult stammerers were also consulted. An 'Agenda of Needs' was compiled and five main issues were identified. These were:

- Talking in school
- Teacher attitudes
- Bullying and teasing
- Oral exams
- Careers advice.

All of these are discussed later in this chapter.

· *Talk to the Teachers* ·

If you are the parent of a child who stammers, the best thing you can do for your son or daughter is to go into the school and speak to the teachers. You need to do this in a business-like way. Make an appointment to see the headteacher as well as the child's class teacher. Ask them to set aside 15 minutes of uninterrupted time for your discussion.

Despite the large number of children who stammer during some part of their school-days, there are teachers who say that they don't remember coming across any children who stammer in the schools in which they have taught. One of the reasons for this may be that stammering varies so much from child to child. Children stammer in different ways (as do adults, of course) and in varying degrees of severity. Also, stammering can vary in different situations. A child may stammer badly in one situation and hardly at all in another. Teachers may not always be able to identify a child stammerer.

Children may very craftily hide their stammer by avoiding certain words and speaking situations. They may also may be clever at hiding their feelings of anger, fear, guilt and shame. They may present as uncooperative or under-achievers or they may become very quiet, 'invisible' pupils. They need bringing out and a sensitive, informed teacher may well be able to do just that.

Try to discuss with the teachers in your child's school some of the general points about stammering. Explain that some children are born with a predisposition to this speech problem. With help, many young children are able to overcome it, but as the child gets older it becomes much more difficult to 'cure' the stammer completely. However, this does not mean that children who stammer cannot learn to speak more fluently or stammer more smoothly. Either way, with help from teachers as well as from home *there is no reason why a child who stammers cannot enjoy every part of school life to the full and achieve as much as any other pupil.*

If your child is seeing a speech and language therapist, tell his or her teachers. The therapist may have some particular information about your child to pass on to the teachers. The therapist may also be able to give advice on how best to handle issues such as assembly, reading aloud in class, demands made by the National Curriculum and so on. In addition, The British Stammering Association has produced information packs relating to primary and secondary school-age children (available from their offices) which you can pass on to your child's school. The Association has made a video entitled *A Chance to Speak* which has been donated to local education authorities for schools to borrow, to help teachers understand the issues.

· *Some Points for Teachers* ·

If you are a teacher, one of the most important points to bear in mind, as research has shown, a number of negative, stereotyped views of stammering children persist. Try to guard against projecting views you may hold of what stammerers are like on to children in your school who stammer. A stammering child may just seem shy, or to have little to say for himself, so the stammer may not be obvious. Another child who stammers, however, may be talkative with people he knows well but very quiet with a new teacher or a pupil he doesn't know.

The severity of stammering can fluctuate. It can become more severe or more fluent for no apparent reason. This unpredictable fluctuation increases the anxiety of the situation for many stammerers.

It is also worth remembering that each person's sensitivity to their stammer varies. A child's anxiety about his stammer will not necessarily be related to the severity of the condition. A child with a fairly mild or moderate stammer may be very sensitive about it and anxious about speaking, whereas one with a severe stammer may be much more outgoing. It is more important to be aware of the level of anxiety in the child rather than the severity of the stammer.

Children are *not* helped by:

- Being forced to speak. Stammering is not due to a lack of practice in speaking.
- Being told to slow down, take deep breaths or think before they speak. Suggestions like these are more likely to make the child nervous and his stammer worse.

Children who stammer may avoid:

- People who ask a lot of questions and always seem to be in a hurry.
- Acknowledging the fact that they stammer.
- Talking about stammering to anyone.

There are some general issues that schoolchildren who stammer would like their teachers to know. The following points have been compiled by pupils themselves.

- Teachers should listen to *what* is being said rather than *how* it is said.
- They should try not to interrupt and try to maintain eye contact as much as possible.
- If there is a particular course of action that the school or the teachers plan to take with regard to the child's stammering, they should discuss it with him or her first. For instance, if the teacher plans to overcome the problem of the register by asking the stammering child to put his hand up or call out his name with a friend, she should consult the child who stammers, in private, first. The youngster may offer a solution that would suit him better.

- If the teachers can work in conjunction with the child's family and speech and language therapist (if there is one), it will ensure that the child makes the best possible progress.

Education is very important for all young people in this increasingly demanding age. For people who stammer, a positive experience of their school-days can have far-reaching future benefits, in terms of their careers as well as their domestic and social lives.

Here are the main issues identified in the Agenda of Needs compiled by The British Stammering Association.

· *Talking in School* ·

Children who stammer may have problems with:

- Answering questions orally
- Reading aloud in class
- Answering the register
- Talking in assembly.

If the school can establish an environment where the child feels safe and confident to speak, despite the fact that he or she stammers, this will, of course, help enormously. If teachers themselves can respond to the child who stammers in a relaxed and patient manner, this is the first step to achieving that goal. If the teacher believes that stammering is nothing remarkable but just something that some children do, she will pass this benign message about stammering on to her pupils.

Talking to the child about his or her feelings about stammering is another important issue. Obviously the teacher has to gauge this carefully and sensitively. Some children may not want to talk about it at all, in which case it is perhaps better not to discuss it. With other children the teacher may have to wait for a suitable opportunity to arise and then introduce the subject in a sensitive way, in private. Some children who stammer may be encouraged by a teacher to talk about stammering in front of their classmates. This can work particularly well if it is introduced in the context of other pupils' problems, so that one child talks about her asthma, another about his eczema, and so on.

Encouraging a child who stammers to contribute in school can improve both his self-esteem and his fluency. However, teachers should always give children the option not to take part in activities with which they clearly cannot cope.

· *Teacher Attitudes* ·

Most teachers are caring about their pupils, particularly those who have special needs. Occasionally teachers are insensitive and dismissive of their pupils who stammer. This may be due to a lack of understanding of the problems of the stammering child or insufficient information on how to cope. The teacher may feel inadequate and diffident about handling the problem, or may not realise that the child stammers. Perhaps the most important point for teachers to bear in mind is that stammering children differ from their peers in one aspect only: their speech. *Intelligence is not affected by stammering.*

The stammering child needs to express himself and take a full and active part in all school activities just as much as a fluent child. He may simply need more help to do so.

First of all, how can teachers recognise that a child in their class or school may have a stammer when it is not obvious? Here are some indications:

- Does the child speak in a tense or jerky way?
- Does his speech seem to embarrass both himself and his listener?
- Does the child seem embarrassed only when he is speaking and much more relaxed at other times?
- Does he seem to avoid certain words, or are his sentences constructed somewhat clumsily, leading the listener to suspect he is avoiding using them?
- Does the child appear to avoid speaking situations?
- When asked questions, particularly in front of others, does the child avoid answering? Perhaps he pretends he hasn't heard or causes some kind of distraction that will 'get him off the hook'.

All these are *possible* indications of stammering.

With many children, their stammer is very obvious. How should teachers respond? Here are some suggestions:

- Try not to correct speech. If you want to help with grammar and pronunciation, just repeat what the child has said in a grammatically correct way.
- Do not interrupt if possible. Every time you interrupt, the child has to start again. Stammering is more severe at the start of speaking and by interrupting you are making things more difficult for the dysfluent pupil.
- Do not suggest that he takes deep breaths or thinks before he speaks. These kinds of suggestion are likely to make him more nervous and aggravate the stammer.

- Do not exclude the young person who stammers from speaking situations. Just try to allow him the time he needs to finish what he is saying.
- Do not finish his sentences for him.
- Do not show him that you are agitated or frustrated with his inability to speak more fluently.
- If he is going through a bad patch of stammering, try to build up his confidence in the things that he does well.
- Try to ensure that the child has an opportunity to say his piece in a non-competitive way. In a discussion group, for instance, it may be very difficult for the stammering child to give his point of view when there are many other children anxious to do the same. If you know there is a child who stammers in this situation, it may be better to invite children to speak by name rather than leaving it as a free-for-all discussion, which may work well in other circumstances.
- *Try to convey to the child that you are not worried about his stammering.*

· *Teasing and Bullying* ·

A child's performance at school can be severely affected by bullying. It is also extremely damaging to the victim's self-confidence and feelings of self-worth. Many children who stammer experience name-calling and mimicking, which does little for their self-esteem. Bullying does not have to be physical. Any aggressive behaviour that is intended to hurt someone can be bullying. It is not difficult to appreciate that children who are persistently bullied do not want to go to school.

Boys and girls bully in different ways. Teasing and name-calling are practised by both boys and girls, but with boys bullying can also take the form of inflicting physical pain. Girls more often resort to spreading hurtful stories which are often untrue, or excluding the victim from group activities.

Fortunately, there has been a great deal of research into bullying at school. Assessments have been made of who the bullies are and why they bully and guidelines for schools on how to cope with bullying have been produced. Schools can do a lot to counteract bullying.

In their leaflet 'Why Bullying Matters', *Young Minds*, the children's mental health charity, comments:

Research shows that when everyone involved with the school – teachers, pupils, parents and non-teaching staff – takes a strong and open stand against bullying, it is far less common. It must be made clear that all pupils have a right not to be bullied. It is especially important that schools encourage pupils to accept that it is not wrong to 'tell'.

However, as the leaflet points out, children need to feel confident that something will be done to stop the bullying.

There are a number of organisations that can help. *Young Minds* can tell you what children's mental health professionals do and where to find help locally. The *Anti-bullying Campaign* is a support service for parents of bullied children. They produce factsheets and guidelines for teachers and also run some regional support services. *Kidscape* is a registered charity which provides leaflets, books, videos and teaching packs on how to deal with bullying. They also run a Parents' Bullying Helpline. If you would like a free copy of their 'You Can Beat Bullying' pack, send them a large self-addressed envelope with two first-class stamps.

The addresses of all the above organisations appear at the end of this book.

The Psychology Department at the University of Sheffield has produced a resource pack on behalf of The British Stammering Association. Its aims are to create a safe and productive learning environment for children who stammer. Although produced mainly for primary-school pupils, it makes interesting reading for those concerned with schoolchildren of all ages. Different approaches to dealing with bullying are briefly outlined in the pack, with references as to where to obtain more detailed information on each of the methods. As an example, there follows a brief rundown of one of these methods.

· *Assertiveness Training* ·

This is intended to show children ways in which they can respond to teasing or bullying situations. Assertive behaviour involves a clear and direct approach in which the bullied pupil stands up for his or her rights without violating those of the other child. The object is to resist the aggressive behaviour without overpowering the perpetrator. Assertiveness training is designed to help the bullied pupil remain calm and neutral while responding to the bully as an equal. The idea is to redress the imbalance of power associated with bullying incidents. The bullied child is helped to broaden his repertoire of possible ways to respond to a given situation. Assertiveness training rarely escalates bullying, but encourages the victim to feel less helpless and more in control. This can of course boost self-confidence and self-esteem, which in itself can diffuse the bullying.

There are four main principles which a pupil can apply to any bullying situation. These are:

- Assess the situation.
- Respond assertively.
- Enlist the support of someone else, either immediately or soon after the incident.
- Leave the situation as soon as possible.

Here are some of the techniques:

Make an assertive statement

The pupil states calmly and clearly how he or she feels about the situation or event, *maintaining eye contact throughout*. This is the example given in the BSA pack:

> 'A pupil who is being pestered by another pupil might say, "I want you to leave me alone." Someone who is being called nasty names could say: 'I don't like it when you call me names. I want you to stop.'

The child may need to repeat the statement once or twice before he is left alone.

If a child is being threatened to do something against his will he could say: 'No. I don't want to.' How he makes this statement is all-important. *He must show that he means it. He must not smile. He must maintain eye contact and talk calmly and clearly.*

The broken record

This is another useful technique, as the BSA pack explains:

> The technique sounds like a record which is stuck, hence the name. A pupil who is being urged to give up their dinner money may repeat the phrase 'I don't give up my dinner money.' The trick is to avoid becoming angry or trying to reason with the bullying pupils and simply stick to the assertive statement.

Pupils will probably need to be shown how to handle any physical intimidation that can occur in these situations. Teachers should help the child to rehearse speaking assertively. They will need to maintain this stance even if the bully comes very close, looks threatening or pushes the pupil.

Handling name-calling

Many children who stammer experience name-calling. Here the trick is for the bullied pupil to appear totally unaffected and calm and respond with such statements as 'You may think so,' 'Maybe' or 'It may look that way to you.' These are neutral statements which do not escalate the situation. They are more likely to bore the bully into going away.

One of the ways in which teachers can help pupils handle name-calling in this calm and detached way is to desensitise the children to the names they are called. Children can become very distressed by these unkind names and find it difficult to repeat them. Role-playing can help. Prepare a set of cards with one nasty name on each card. Each pupil then selects two or three of these names to use in the role-play.

Staying calm

This is the key to assertive behaviour, but it is very hard to remain calm in a threatening situation. Some children may find relaxation or stress-management techniques helpful.

Assertiveness techniques can be taught as part of the main curriculum, with the teacher demonstrating the approach to the whole class. Pupils can be put into pairs or threes to practise and then the whole class or small groups can discuss the effectiveness of the exercise.

Sometimes it can be useful to set up a small group for children who have experienced bullying. Group meetings provide a safe arena in which children can talk about what has happened to them as well as practising and developing techniques to combat future bullying. The members of the group can be very supportive of each other. It is important for teachers to be careful in choosing the children who will be involved. An ideal number is considered to be between six and eight, and, although it can be a mixed age group, it is easier when the children are of a similar level of language ability and maturity. It should be borne in mind that the group will take time to gel as the children get to know each other. Some children may be disruptive in this new group situation.

Assertiveness techniques can also be taught on a one-to-one basis. The teacher will need to set aside time to meet with the child and possibly the child's friend. In this kind of setting the adult will need to change roles with the child. Thus the teacher plays the bullied pupil and the child plays the bully. This allows the teacher to demonstrate the techniques that need to be learnt.

Whichever setting is chosen, the basic approach remains the same:

- The child observes the technique.
- He then practises it several times and adapts the technique to one he feels comfortable with. He is given feedback on his use of the skill to help him refine it.
- The child is taught the importance of eye contact and body language as well as the words being spoken.
- The pupil should be given opportunities to discuss how the technique could be used.

For further information about the BSA pack, which is entitled 'Bullying and the Dysfluent Child in Primary School', contact the Association's head office in London (see Useful Addresses).

· *Oral Exams* ·

Students who stammer, their parents and teachers can ensure that the necessary arrangements are made to provide for a stammering child's special needs. These may include:

- Extra time to cater for the dysfluency of the candidate.
- Special tuition. In order to prepare adequately for the exam, the pupil may need to be coached by a teacher or a speech and language therapist.

It is important for examiners to put to one side a child's dysfluency and to focus only on the child's capabilities in the examination subject.

· *Careers Advice* ·

Stammerers hold down jobs successfully in all aspects of working life. The stories of Robin and David which appear in Chapters Six and Seven are two cases in point. Robin has enjoyed a successful career as a lecturer. David is an air traffic controller, a very verbal job which requires his speech to be precise and on time. Both men are stammerers.

However, no two people who stammer are alike. While some may excel in positions that demand good communication skills because they enjoy the challenge, others may shy away from careers that place such a large emphasis on speech. Also, there may be some jobs that are not suitable for severe stammerers. Careers advice should be based on a realistic assessment of the individual's needs and abilities.

· *James* ·

I cannot remember ever speaking fluently. I was told that I started stammering when I was about five or six years old. My mother had a really bad stammer until she was 20 and then it just vanished. She still stammers occasionally on a single word.

I don't think it bothered me much when I was very young but when I went to middle school it really got to me. It wasn't because I was teased. I had friends. It was the way I felt inside. I think it was the way I thought that other people must feel about me.

I felt I wasn't normal. Reading out in class was bad but I think it was more to do with the frustration of not being able to say what I actually wanted to say. So I often found myself saying something else. I'd end up finding other words which were easier.

There was another stammerer at my middle school. He wanted to be friends with me, but I didn't want that. I suppose when I spoke to him it was like speaking to myself and I didn't like that. I think I wanted to disassociate from the stammering. I didn't want to have anything to do with him. Even now one of the worst things for me is watching other people stammer. I find it very difficult.

I had good friends at school and no one who would have seen me could have suspected that there was anything wrong. It was all on the inside, really. But there were times when my mother used to drive me into school and I'd say that I didn't want to go in and I'd say things like I wanted to kill myself. Of course my mum got very upset.

I ended up seeing psychiatrists and we had family therapy. I found out afterwards that they diagnosed that some time during that period I had a nervous breakdown. I think it was caused by the fact that I could not communicate what I wanted to say. I felt very, very low at that time but I kept it mostly to myself.

I didn't go to school for almost a year. During that time I saw a speech therapist and a hypnotherapist as well as other complementary therapists. Eventually my parents decided to send me to a small private school, which worked out all right. I hadn't accepted the stammering, but I came to terms with the fact that I had to go to school and get an education.

I did my GCSEs and my A levels. From the time of my 'breakdown' onwards stammering was not mentioned at all in the house. I think my parents could see that I didn't like talking about it. Perhaps it was because I didn't want to think about what had happened during the time I was at middle school. But I still don't like talking about it very much.

I went to university and studied computing. I made some very good friends there. But it never leaves you. Stammering is on my mind all the time. It is very frustrating. In every situation I am constantly thinking ahead to what might happen. If I know I might be in a situation where I may have to speak, I sometimes avoid that situation.

Having to speak unexpectedly is the worst. For example, if I'm walking along a street and someone asks me for directions, it's bad because it's instant and it's a stranger as well.

At university it was all right. When I was two years into my course I saw a speech therapist. She tried some of the usual speech therapy techniques. It didn't actually help the stammer in any physical way, but it was good to be able to talk to somebody about it after such a long time. I hadn't spoken to anyone about my stammering for around eight years.

If I drink I always end up fluent. After a few drinks I can speak all evening. I met this girl one evening when I was out. I had been drinking and I was fluent and it went really well. We arranged to go out the following evening. It was early on in the evening when we met up. I hadn't been drinking and I wasn't very fluent. When she heard that I had a stammer she didn't want to have anything to do with me. It puts me off asking girls out. One of the things that is awkward is finding a relationship.

I don't think I'll ever come to terms with stammering. I know that I have it and I'm okay about speaking but it is still very frustrating.

If a few years ago someone had told me that at the age of 22 I'd have a good degree, a good job and be living in a flat of my own, I may not have believed them. But it is exactly where I am now. It has given me a little more confidence.

5

TEENAGERS WHO STAMMER

Adolescence is often a difficult and painful time in the life cycle of a human being. It is a period of both mental and physical change. Young people want to try new things and may be starting to break free of their dependency on their parents. During the teenage years, perhaps more than ever, there is an enormous amount of peer pressure. And it comes at a time when the young person may not be at all sure who he is and what he wants to be. Being socially acceptable is something that most of us want, whatever our age, but during the teenage years it can be of paramount importance.

As a young person, you may want, along with social acceptability, to establish your own individuality. It can sometimes be a difficult tightrope to walk. Talking and exchanging ideas; discussing school, dating, your parents, your friends, your future, are all essential to the growing-up process. You will probably want to be accepted for who you are and for your own unique personality and not to be thought of as different from your peers.

For a person who stammers, adolescence can be particularly frustrating. It may be the first time that you have faced up to the condition. Perhaps throughout childhood you were told that you would grow out of it: 'Give it time, and it will go away.' But it has not. Suddenly, at the age of 14 or 15, the realisation dawns on you that the stammer is here to stay. It is not going to miraculously disappear. It can be a time of uncertainty and challenge. The booklet, 'Do you Stutter? A Guide for Teens', produced by the Stuttering Foundation of America, makes the point:

> If you are a teenager who stutters there are going to be some problems that are uniquely yours . . . . At one time or another everyone in the world feels stupid, weak, worthless, ashamed, resentful, angry, fearful, or a little weird. If you stutter, however, it is tempting to believe that you feel this way because of stuttering.

The booklet is available from the BSA.

Many teenagers who stammer become withdrawn. They do not know who to turn to or where to ask for help. When they were children, stammering may never have been discussed, either at home or at school. You may have hidden your stammer and spent your childhood covering your tracks, speaking very little and always rehearsing and avoiding the words you find difficult. You may have presented yourself as a non-stammerer. People may think that you are quiet or someone who doesn't have much to say for himself.

When we reach decisions about the things we like and dislike about ourselves, we usually start trying to stop doing the things we dislike. For people who stammer this may mean trying to stop stammering. It is normal to want to speak naturally and easily. At school in particular, it is hard not being like everyone else. But having a stammer does not mean that you do not have the right to speak as much as the next person. Avoiding speaking and avoiding stammering, even avoiding words or sounds which you have particular trouble with, will make approaching these things harder the next time you try.

Your teenage years can be a time of enormous change and upheaval and will probably affect the role you play within your family, especially your relationship with your parents. A common problem among teenagers who stammer is the difficulty of moving away from the protective influence of their parents, especially in speaking situations. Your parents may be used to doing a lot of things for you, like making difficult phone calls or even speaking for you in certain situations. Maybe you think that stammering is something your parents don't want to talk about, or that it makes them irritated or angry? Perhaps you are concerned that your parents do not really seem to understand just how much your stammer affects your life? You may even feel that you have let them down?

You are not alone in having these feelings. Talk to your parents, no matter how much you stammer, and tell them how you feel. Let them know what they can do to help and make it clear that it is important to you that you do your own talking. You may be surprised by how pleased they are to be included and to be told how they can help you. By discussing your stammering openly, you are already climbing one of the biggest hurdles of all.

School is another place where you could discuss stammering with your fellow pupils and teachers. If you find it difficult to read aloud in class or are worried about oral exams, you should talk to your teacher. There may be a simple way in which things can be made easier for you, without drawing attention to yourself in the classroom. Your stammer will be less of an issue for your friends and classmates if it is not a big issue to you. Acknowledging the fact that you have a stammer is definitely better than pretending it does not exist and (although not all stammering teenagers get teased) it also discourages ridicule.

Many teenagers who have no speech problems experience embarrassment and diffidence in approaching members of the opposite sex, particularly somebody they are attracted to. Julian, whose personal account appears in Chapter Six, says:

> It was always a great problem for me as a teenager, liking girls and admiring them, but not being able to approach them and speak to them for fear of sounding absolutely stupid. As a teenager, I had a terrible stammer with head-jerking, facial tics and everything else which generally now I have under control. But as a teenager, without any experience of speech therapy, it wasn't under control at all. It was extremely embarrassing and frustrating and I just didn't know which way to turn. I think that's a terrific problem for teenagers who stammer.

Stammering may affect relationships, but not always in the way you think. If you stammer a lot, you will usually talk less than a fluent person. As a result, you may not have developed your conversational skills. Working on your speech will give you a chance to practise.

Along with the biological changes, there are those going on in your head. The need for self-expression makes itself felt. You want to talk, to socialise and make yourself known. You also have many other practical considerations which will almost certainly include education and choice of career.

The prospect of going to interviews or pursuing a career may be the trigger that starts you worrying about your stammer. You may not have thought about it much before. You may have got by without any major problems concerning your speech condition. But now you have to go out and find a job in a competitive world where people do not know you and are not familiar with your stammer. The good news in this daunting scenario is that it usually takes just such a trigger to get people working on their speech. Complacency changes nothing, but a little anxiety can sometimes lead to a great improvement.

Some of you will want to work on accepting and modifying your stammering. Even though you may still stammer a little you will develop a confident attitude about talking. Others will want to work more directly on eliminating their stammering, using a technique like slow prolonged speech. Although fluency can be achieved by this method, it can sound a bit unnatural and is hard to keep up all the time.

Whatever approach or combination of approaches you use, it is important to remember that making any changes to yourself, no matter how desirable, can be a difficult task. Do not expect overnight success, but congratulate yourself for any progress you make, no matter how small it may seem.

According to The British Stammering Association, therapy can:

- Help you to learn more about yourself, your stammering and the effect these have on your life, enabling you to take responsibility for your problem and deal with it as you see fit, thus helping you to achieve your future potential.
- Enable you and your parents to cope better with your speech difficulties and with your own developing maturity.
- Address issues to do with school, teachers and friends. It will help you to understand the problems you may have with your stammering and to develop strategies which will improve your confidence in dealing with them.
- Put speech techniques in perspective, to see whether certain speech skills can be taught and used successfully in everyday life.

Stammering is a problem that can affect every aspect of your life, the BSA maintains. This is why speech and language therapy must address every angle, help you to help yourself in developing confidence, social skills, self-awareness and problem-solving strategies.

By the time you become a teenager, stammering is not just a speech problem. It is a combination of different things, and in order to tackle it effectively you may need to look at other aspects of your life as well as your speech. This will be different for each individual.

Some speech and language therapists have a variety of ideas up their sleeves. Some of them run special groups for teenagers where they can talk freely in a safe and confidential environment. They can practise speech techniques with a receptive and supportive audience and discuss their problems with people who know exactly how they feel.

Peggy Dalton, a speech and language therapist, says she enjoys working with teenagers and works with them in a much more flexible way than with other age groups.

Much of the work is aimed at preventing the build-up of avoidance. The sessions are usually in a group. People talk about what stammering means to them and how it affects their lives; they can discuss painful as well as happy experiences.

Role-play is often used, mainly to build up confidence to do everyday things that some stammerers find difficult, such as buying tickets, taking things back to a shop, saying no, and being assertive. This is sometimes followed up with assignment work. For instance, youngsters may be sent off to do in real life some of the things they have practised in the sessions. They will often carry out these assignments in pairs so that they can support each other. They are encouraged to tackle the task despite their stammer, and the goal is to build up confidence, not to achieve perfection.

Another method that Peggy sometimes uses is to get her young clients to draw their stammer:

> One older teenager drew a little figure on a tightrope with fire and horrible stuff underneath. Another girl drew herself looking in a mirror. She had no mouth. Another drew herself sitting in front of a telephone and there were a whole lot of people sitting behind her with great big staring eyes, obviously looking and listening. They can often draw it better than they can tell it. But having drawn it they can more easily talk about it to each other. Sometimes a young person will draw something that they cannot put into words.

Rehearsing and role-playing interviews can also be part of the therapy sessions. In fact, a lot of work is done on interview techniques. One of the issues that comes up is whether or not to tell a prospective employer that you have a stammer. Peggy recalls:

> There was one young chap who was dying to go into one of the Services. He was a personable young man with quite a severe persistent stammer. What he didn't want to do was to mention his stammer. I suggested that he might either say something about it on the form he filled in or he could mention it at the start of the interview, or if he got into difficulty, he might say something like 'As you can see, I've got a stammer.' The important thing is to acknowledge it. Don't pretend it's not there.

If you do not mention your stammer, the prospective employer may feel awkward about bringing up the subject. This means that it will not be discussed and, if the employer has any misgivings about taking on someone who stammers, you will have done nothing to allay his fears.

If you are the parent of a teenager who stammers, bear in mind that it is not the severity of your child's stammer that is the important issue, but his or her feelings about it. Your child is going through possibly the most sensitive period of his life. A mild stammer may appear as an enormous disability to someone of this age. Try to accept the problem from your child's viewpoint. Encourage him to talk about it and listen to what he has to say. He will undoubtedly value your help and support even though he may not show it.

If you are a teenager who stammers, it may be hard for you to be open about stammering with those around you. It is probably harder still to talk about your fears and worries concerning your speech to anyone but your closest friends. Stammering may not be something that you are particularly proud of but it *is* a part of you and, like every other part, deserves your attention and respect. Just because you are a stammerer, you do not have any less right to speak out in the classroom, at home or with friends than a fluent speaker. So start talking.

You may find some of the other chapters in this book of interest. Chapter One explains some of the theories about stammering, which may be helpful when you talk about it to other people. The chapters on school and work may be helpful, too, as should Chapter Six: Adults Who Stammer. Also look at Chapter Ten for tips on how you can help yourself on your own.

· *Lisa* ·

Lisa is slowly coming to terms with her life as a person who stammers. She has gained an enormous amount from attending courses and workshops for people who stammer at the City Literary Institute in London.

During her teenage years Lisa always believed that with enough hard work she could cure herself. However, she was unsuccessful in achieving this with either slow prolonged speech or hypnotherapy.

When I was 15 I finally convinced my GP that hypnotherapy was going to cure me of my stammer. I believed in this more than anyone. I had read books on the subject, they told me that it was all about belief. Speech therapy had been a bit like this too: 'You won't get better if you don't practise.' I'd been going since I was five, I didn't practise enough and I never got better. My therapist would teach me new ways of speaking: slowly; softly; slurring; taking deep breaths; speaking with a metronome, and when I did what she said I never stammered. It was amazing and it worked. The problem was I felt ridiculous. She told me that I had to practise these new ways of speaking with my friends and family. When I said that they made me feel stupid she said: 'But doesn't stammering make you feel like that too?'

Was I lazy? Weak? I had a problem, someone had shown me a way of overcoming it. Why did I choose to keep my problem? I realised recently that I stammered, not by choice, but because I couldn't help it. But what if I was to choose to speak in a different way, the way I had been taught by my speech therapist? I would stop stammering, but what would they think, my audience? 'Is she deliberately speaking in that strange way?' What a fear that was. In moments of frustration, my father would sometimes say to me: 'Sometimes I think that you're doing it on purpose.' I wasn't, and I wasn't ready to start doing anything on purpose that would make me feel different or encourage attention. That was exactly what speech therapy was asking me to do. Hypnotherapy asked similar things of me. Belief and hard work would lead to a cure. I believed and I worked but I was never cured and I blamed myself for that.

Just before I went to comprehensive school we had moved to a new town. I was about 11. Everything in school felt hard: saying the register, asking a simple question. I hated my stammer then. I never learned French or German and I didn't speak unless I absolutely had to. It took a couple of years before I started making some good friends. I had learnt to hide my stammer as much as I could. I avoided saying words I thought I might have trouble with, I rearranged sentences. If I couldn't say the word I wanted, sometimes I would pretend I couldn't remember it. I played charades with my friends, 'One word, two syllables' and so on. It made them laugh and that felt good. When a teacher asked me what my name was, I would pretend that I had forgotten it. I was playing up, I'd get detention and I'd make my friends laugh. All this seemed infinitely better than stammering. When I did get caught out, I would ridicule myself, make people laugh about my stammer, tell jokes, put on accents – all of which, incidentally, would help me speak more fluently. This was fine in some respects and I think it did me a lot of good at the time. It made me happy; it gave me confidence. But the truth was I wasn't always happy and light-hearted and I didn't always feel like telling jokes.

I could never discover an absolute cure. There seemed so many different things which brought on my stammering: tiredness, stress, excitement, and yet there were also times I was tired, stressed, excited, when I spoke with perfect fluency. I did have the ability to speak. How was it that sometimes I lost that ability? When I was small I had learnt to ride a bike. I had never forgotten how to ride that bike. Why was speaking so different?

I am 27 now and speech therapy has changed a lot over the last few years. I used to think that stammering was something which happened to me, but I have been encouraged to see stammering as a part of me and to try and work with it and not against it.

We have many choices in our lives and sometimes we forget this and let other people make all the choices for us. But we stammer and we cannot choose not to. We can choose to fight our stammering and constantly fail or we can choose to stammer. It's difficult, but worth it.

6

ADULTS WHO STAMMER

Approximately one in every hundred adults stammers. It is a male-dominated condition, affecting almost four men to every woman. Stammering can sometimes run in families. If a parent stammers, there is a slightly increased risk of having a stammering child. Even if the parent stops stammering long before the child is born, a genetic predisposition towards problems in speech and language development remains and may lead to the child starting to stammer. It is thought that if one identical twin stammers, the chance that the other one will too is over 70 per cent.

Stammering has no bearing on a person's IQ. On the whole stammerers are as capable and intelligent as non-stammerers. Being unable to put across your point of view when you speak does not mean that you haven't got one or that it isn't both intelligent and considered. Many highly creative people stammer. For example, in the literary field, both Lewis Carroll, the author of *Alice's Adventures in Wonderland*, and the poet Philip Larkin stammered.

People stammer in different ways and have different problems. Some have difficulty reading aloud or answering the telephone, while others do not. Some find that they can speak fairly fluently if they are lecturing or giving a speech, while for others this would be a terrifying ordeal. Robin, who features in this chapter, has spent much of his life working as a lecturer. Margaret, (see Chapter One) gave up taking an active role in her local Townswomen's Guild because of the trauma of public speaking. Under the influence of alcohol, some people stammer more, whereas others become much more fluent. James, in Chapter Four, says: 'After a few drinks, I can speak all evening.' Very few people who stammer have any difficulty when they sing or read aloud with others.

Although people who stammer may have built up some emotional and psychological problems around stammering, this does not mean that they are any more emotionally or psychologically dysfunctional than anyone else. In the same way as someone suffering from severe eczema or psoriasis may have hang-ups about the appearance of his skin, someone who stammers may be sensitive about his speech. This is perfectly normal.

People who stammer in adulthood are very rarely cured completely, although the stammer sometimes gradually disappears as they become more confident. However, by and large the propensity to stammer is always there. This is because of all the emotional and psychological issues that surround the issue of stammering. It is no longer just a physical thing, but a psychological one as well.

In a very young child, stammering nearly always starts off as a behavioural, technical difficulty. Children stumble over their words. They are not expected to be fluent: quite the contrary, a degree of dysfluency is sometimes considered 'cute' in a very young child.

The older you get, the more the psychological issues are involved. A child of 12 may have already begun to define himself as 'a stammerer' and to anticipate his life in terms of stammering. Will he be able to manage this or that? Will that person be frightening? Will this person or that situation make him stammer?

Some people who stammer or block consistently are so embarrassed and humiliated by it that they feel helpless, inadequate and depressed. Many stammerers feel different from other people and set apart from the rest of society. The wall that separates them from people who speak freely seems impenetrable, but it isn't.

Nearly all stammerers have periods of fluency. Many are perfectly fluent when talking to their pets or members of their family. Once they get into outside situations where they are expected to be fluent, the stammer perversely reappears.

One theory is that the desire to speak without stammering is so strong that they try to force a degree of fluency they cannot possibly achieve. This creates tension in their speech mechanism, which makes the stammering worse.

The ability to speak fluently in completely relaxed situations gives rise to the belief that stammering in adulthood is more to do with what is built up around the stammer than the speech defect itself. This does not mean that there is no point tackling the dysfluency. There are enormous benefits to be gained in dealing with the speech problems, but there are other options as well.

Pressure, fear and anticipation of failure all combine to produce the stammer in certain situations. And they are not imaginary fears; they're real. If you have always stammered when saying your name, talking to strangers, asking for what you want and explaining yourself, it's a reality. Over the years your sense of yourself will have been formed around stammering, particularly in those situations. You will expect to have problems with speech in those areas, but you may also expect to be fluent in others.

· *Covert and Overt Stammering* ·

You will also have developed strategies to cope with stammering, some of which will have become so ingrained that you may not be fully aware that they exist. This adds to the submerged part of your personal stammering iceberg referred to in Chapter One. Some people go through most of their lives hiding their stammer. These *covert* stammerers will have spent their childhood acquiring phenomenal skills in changing words and sentences to avoid blocking or stammering on words that they find difficult. Clearly, these are intelligent people, but they do themselves a disservice because they don't tackle the problem in a real way. Neither do they manage to say what they want to say when they want to say it.

In Chapter Four, James says that he had a nervous breakdown as a child because he became so frustrated with not being able to express himself adequately.

The truth of the matter is that even fluent speakers aren't able to say what they want with the kind of ease that many stammerers perceive. Even if you do not have a speech problem, it is very hard to convey your exact thoughts to your listener. How many times have you heard someone say: 'That isn't what I meant'? Most of us cannot instantaneously call up the right vocabulary. It is difficult to be verbally coherent and precise. But this doesn't stop most people from talking!

If you spend your time substituting words, you are limiting your vocabulary. You are giving yourself less of a chance to express yourself accurately. And if you also rephrase your sentences, it is likely that what you are saying may be quite different from what you want to say. Fear and avoidance of aspects of speech can be very distancing. A person who is hiding his stammer may also be hiding himself. He may not get very close to people because he believes he cannot talk to them and because he doesn't want them to discover his stammer.

Nevertheless, speech and language therapists say that working with covert stammerers can be very satisfying. Once they summon up the courage to speak and start to change some of their old habits of avoidance, a transformation often takes place.

Others do not hide their stammer but they impose serious limitations on their lives. They may be *overt* stammerers, in the sense that people are aware that they stammer, but they too can spend a lot of time hiding.

'I cannot recall travelling on a train anywhere on my own until I was about 43 or 44,' says David Preece, who is an active member of The British Stammering Association.

It would have meant going to a station and asking for a ticket. Prior to any sort of speech therapy that would have been impossible for me to do. I would have stammered over it. It sounds ridiculous now, but it's true. Lots of people are isolated. They feel that because they stammer they cannot do things. They may be interested in a particular activity but they feel that they cannot take part in it because they'll stammer.

It is extremely isolating. It handicaps career prospects. People often don't apply for particular jobs knowing that it is a job they could do and one that they would be interested in, but they don't believe they will get through the interview. They can't face it.

Although he is still a stammerer, David's speech is much more fluent now and he says he feels confident about speaking in any situation:

I was almost 44 before I went to a speech therapist. I was so isolated that I had never even heard of speech therapy. When I did hear of it, I couldn't bring myself to begin to find out about it because the prospect was so scary.

I'm sure lots of people who stammer hide behind the stammer like I used to and then begin to blame everything that happens to them on the stammer, and that is self-destructive as well.

Long-established perceptions and behaviour patterns can be difficult to shift. Often they fulfil a certain purpose in the person's life. Many people admit to hiding behind their stammer, for example. Some may also accept that there are aspects of stammering they rely on and, although they may not welcome the stammer, they may enjoy certain benefits from hiding behind it.

For instance, if you have always been accepted as being a person who does not speak in certain situations, you may have been shielded from some ugly scenes and difficult tasks. Confrontational situations would not have been your domain. Your partner would have been the one to return faulty goods, have rows with tradesmen over bad service and complain about the phone bill, for instance. If you start to speak more confidently and are able to answer the phone and book the holiday, your partner may suggest that *you* have that delicate talk with the bank manager, or tell the double-glazing salesman not to call back – ever!

One interviewee said that as he became more fluent more doors were open to him. Although there were aspects of this that he welcomed, he also found it terrifying. A practical and creative man, he had spent much of his non-working life making things. He had also worked very hard at his job, which did not require much speech, and had made a success of that. He wondered whether he would have been so successful had he not stammered and not had to focus on the things he could do without speaking.

Many adults who stammer have spent a great deal of time from their childhood onwards controlling their environment as well as their speech. They will have taken great pains not to put themselves in situations that might require them to speak spontaneously. This kind of control may or may not have become part of their nature, but they are likely to have become used to living and working, for the most part, in situations that are under their control. They tend not to seek out new opportunities and experiences. Suddenly, when speech is no longer such a problem, they find doors opening to them that didn't exist before. These new horizons can feel every bit as daunting as they are exciting.

Learning to speak more freely, whether this is achieved through increased fluency or because of a lessening in concern over fluency, requires a lot of adjustment. This is not limited to the speech itself. Just tackling the physical aspect of stammering is often not enough to maintain the improvement that many stammerers experience when they first go for therapy. Many people will say that the treatment they tried worked for a few weeks but then the improvement started to recede and they were more or less back to where they began. Many adult stammerers have found that the condition responds best when it is treated on the emotional as well as the physical level.

· *The Stammering Hexagon* ·

John C. Harrison is a member of the National Stuttering Project in America. Although he stammered as a child and as a young adult, he now enjoys a fluency that many non-stammerers would envy. John holds the view that stammering is an entity made up of various parts. These include beliefs, intentions, emotions and perceptions as well as physical behaviours and physiological responses.

At an open meeting arranged by The British Stammering Association in London, John outlined his theory:

When I was growing up, my stammering was in the form of a silent block. When I came into my twenties I did a lot of self-therapy and began to understand what I was doing when I was blocking. As a child I had never understood the behavioural aspects of the problem. Stammering was just something that happened to me. But understanding the mechanics of the block didn't in itself change the behaviour. Even though I knew what I was doing, I still couldn't stop myself from blocking in stressful situations.

As a young adult, I embarked on a session of personal growth activities and programmes. During this process, my stammering slowly melted away. En route, one of the big discoveries I made was that my concept of stammering had not been broad enough to contain the solution. There were too many questions that my traditional point of view had not been able to explain. I was looking at stammering through too narrow a window.

Nor was I the only one who had a limited perspective. There were the psychologists who said stammering was a psychological problem. There were the behaviourists who said that it was a question of incorrect behaviours. There were sociologists who said it was a sociological problem. What I began to see was that people perceived the problem through their own particular window. But there were always some questions about stammering that couldn't be answered.

What seems to have eluded everyone, including me for so many years, was that stammering does not exist except as a collection of physical behaviours, emotions, perceptions, beliefs, intentions and physiological responses that come together in a particular way – in what I call the Stammering Hexagon. All parts affect, and are affected by, all the other parts.

Stammering exists when basic aspects of the individual, aspects that are present in all of us, interact and create a 'critical mass'. The system-like nature of stammering – using base parts to create an exotic structure – explains why, when psychological tests are done on stammerers and members of the general population, they find that there is no difference between stammerers and other people.

I have always considered myself a good observer. As I started to observe myself in day-to-day activities and especially in all the personal growth seminars I attended, I began to see things about myself that had heretofore eluded my awareness.

I had a self-assertion problem. I was afraid to speak up for what I wanted. I had an identity problem. I had spent so many years trying to

Stammering Hexagon

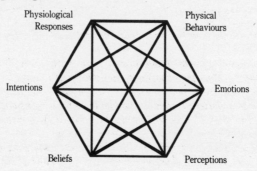

please others that I didn't know who I was. My self-image was highly constricted and denied expression to large sections of my real self. I was afraid to show people what I felt. I was 31 years old before I actually allowed myself to express my anger at another human being.

I had problems with my perceptions and beliefs, interpreting my world in ways that created undue stress.

I began to notice that my stammering was not a unitary problem but actually a collection of issues in a particular kind of relationship. My physical behaviours (stammering blocks) were certainly a part of it. But when I blocked and couldn't say a word, it was also because of how I was seeing and creating my world and all the various ways in which I was holding myself back.

As I became involved in a series of personal growth programmes, my long-lost emotions started to emerge. My self-perceptions also began to change, as did the way I experienced others. Also, my intentions became less conflicted.

To illustrate the effect of conflicting intentions, imagine that your favourite horse has broken its leg and you have to dispatch him. He has been your best friend for 10 years, and you are now pointing a pistol at his head. You want to pull the trigger to put him out of his misery, but at the same time, you don't want to pull the trigger, because he'll be gone from your life forever. The more you try to pull the trigger, the more your finger freezes. This is a classic block, and it happens in any situation where you have conflicting intentions of equal strength pulling at each other. If, furthermore, you are unaware that you have these conflicting attitudes and emotions, the block will appear to be outside your control. Similarly, you can have an intention to speak and an intention not to speak which will cause you to mysteriously block at a particular feared word or in a feared situation.

As I began to understand what stammering was all about, I started putting myself in situations that were both risky and safe so I could observe and address how I functioned in them.

For example, I signed up for a Dale Carnegie programme where, each evening, I had an opportunity to give two impromptu presentations for about 75 seconds each. After every talk I received strong applause, and then received only positive feedback from the instructor. I had never had a positive speaking experience in my life until I attended that class, and the effects stayed with me.

I also joined the Toastmasters' Club and remained active for over two years.

The personal growth programmes were particularly important, because they gave me the opportunity to explore my feelings in a totally safe environment (safe, that is, except to my negative self-image). Being proactive was important because I could go to all the lectures and read all the books, but unless I actually placed myself into a life situation where something could happen, I ended up remaining stuck.

Through all these activities, I was affecting the Stammering Hexagon at many points of the system: emotions, perceptions, beliefs and intentions. Had I just gone to a speech therapist, worked only on my speech, and not done anything to affect all the other Hexagon points, my physical and physiological (panic) responses would have remained very much the same. I had to change the entire system.

Why was this?

Any living system maintains what is called a state of homeostasis, which is the ability or tendency of an organism or a cell to maintain internal equilibrium by adjusting its physiological processes. All the parts of the system want to stay in balance (which is why you shiver when you're cold; shivering allows you to build your body heat back up.) Thus, if you have set up a stammering system and address just one little part of it (your speech) without addressing the other parts, the system will want to re-establish itself by bringing back the old speech behaviours. This is why people so often slip back into stammering after undergoing a therapy programme. They've thrown the system out of balance by changing just a piece of it.

As I continued to let myself out of the box and take risks, my stammering system as a whole started to break apart, slowly dissolving through a steady flow of small but significant changes all around the system. Discovering the system-like nature of stammering allowed me to exert leverage on the problem in many different ways, rather than just working on my speech.

It's never too late to start visualising, hoping and dreaming about things that you want to do. You have to be willing to stay in touch and keep your dreams alive; to not always play it safe, but to venture outside your comfort zone and try new things. You need especially to be willing to extend the paradigm of stammering and look in places for answers where you haven't been looking before. You must become a good observer.

To illustrate why stammering has been such a mystery for so long, consider the example of a man who was walking down the street at night and saw another person on his hands and knees, apparently looking for something under a street light. He asked the searcher what he was looking for. The searcher said that he had lost his car keys.

'Where did you lose them?' asked the pedestrian.

The searcher pointed to where his car was parked a few yards away where it was pitch black.

'I think I lost them there,' the searcher replied.

'Then why are you looking here?' asked the pedestrian.

The searcher replied: 'Because the light is better.'

People have always looked in obvious places for the answers to their stammering, because those areas were in the light and easily visible. But, from my experience, the answers lie in the dark, in the unexplored areas of the self that also relate to self-expression. The answers lie not just in the stammering behaviours, but in one's emotions, perceptions, beliefs and intentions and in how all the elements of the system play upon one another.

This is the importance of adopting a new paradigm to explain chronic stammering, one that is broad enough to contain the answers we have been searching for.

· *Defining and Tackling the Problem* ·

Some stammerers have said that one of the most irritating things people tell them is that they are exaggerating the problem. They may have been told that they don't stammer very much and so shouldn't worry about it, or that everyone has problems; they stammer, so what?

The fact of the matter is that no one can dictate to you the significance of your speech condition. You know what it means to you and only you know what effect it has on your life. Unfortunately, it is also true that you, and only you, can bring about an improvement in your speech.

They say that the journey of a thousand miles begins with a single step. With stammering, a good first step would be to define the problem as you see it. Chapter Ten gives you some guidelines on how to define your stammer.

Along with the physical aspects, try to take a closer look at the emotional and psychological input that stammering has on you. Remember to consider the part of the stammering iceberg that is submerged as well as the bit that is visible. It may help you to draw your own iceberg and list the emotions below the surface. These may include feelings of low self-esteem, unworthiness, fear of people and situations, feeling disadvantaged at having been given a raw deal because of the stammering and so on. You may also want to think about your childhood experiences within or outside your family that may have helped keep the stammer in place or even exaggerated it. This is not a blame-provoking exercise, but one intended to help you look at the problem as a whole and not just the physical part of it.

You may like to flesh out John Harrison's Stammering Hexagon. What are the particular emotions, perceptions, beliefs, intentions, physical behaviours and physiological responses that come together to make up your stammer? Maybe, as John suggests, the time has come to look in the more obscure places for the answers and not just in the obvious ones.

In considering these issues you may be able to judge more clearly how to go about treating the condition.

Do you feel, for instance, that tackling the speech part is most important for you? Do you find it difficult to think about, let alone speak about, emotional things? Do you feel that if you could just speak more fluently the rest would take care of itself?

If this is the case, working on your speech should become your priority. You will need to work hard and practice regularly, but if you have enough dedication there is no reason why you should not achieve a higher level of fluency by focusing primarily on your speech. There are many intensive courses available to help you do just this. The British Stammering Association can put you in touch with those currently on offer. The main thing to remember with intensive courses is that you will have to keep up the motivation to practise long after the course has finished. Many people go on several courses over a few years to improve on their fluency and to keep themselves motivated to practise the techniques.

Your GP will be able to refer you to a speech and language therapist in your area who may see you individually or as part of a group. Many therapists these days employ an eclectic approach to treat stammerers, which means that they use a variety of techniques directed at the speech as well as the emotional and psychological conflicts surrounding it.

You can also contact The British Stammering Association to find out the names of therapists in your area. Therapy is available under the NHS and in some areas through centres of further education.

You may find it useful to join a self-help group if there is one operating in your area. These are run by people who stammer. It is worth overcoming any initial diffidence about joining a group where you don't know anyone. Bear in mind that most people in these groups are stammerers who will understand your fears and hesitancy. Often sharing and discussing the problem with empathetic strangers can be very helpful and can ease the problem. Again, the BSA will be able to tell you if there are any self-help groups in your area. There is more about self-help groups in Chapter Ten.

Many people who stammer feel that the problem is not so much with their speech but with their reluctance to speak. They are less worried about becoming fluent than about feeling free to speak despite the fact that they stammer. The belief here is that the stammer is part of themselves and their personality and something that they don't particularly want to change or control. *They just don't want it to stand in the way of normal living.* They are concerned with what is going on below the level of visibility in the stammering iceberg rather than what is on show.

Some people find that attending intensive courses or other forms of group speech therapy gives them the confidence to become more outgoing and seek more opportunities to speak outside their usual environment. Meeting other people who stammer makes them feel less isolated and 'different' and gives them the impetus to move on. Often, even though they may come away from the course with no improvement to their speech whatever, they will believe themselves to be more fluent because their perception of their speech and, perhaps, their belief in themselves have changed. So they will communicate more freely and may lead more fulfilling lives.

For other people, the shift inside may have to be tackled in another way. They may need to take a closer look at who they are and how they feel at a deeper level. This is where the talking treatments like psychotherapy come in. The aim of this therapy is to help us examine our lives and try to find out why we do the things we do. Other talking treatments work in a similar way. Personal Construct Psychology, for example, is explained in Chapter Eight.

Chapter Ten details some of the self-help techniques you can practise at home to improve your speech and Chapter Eleven outlines some ways in which you can ease the stress and tension of everyday living with therapies that teach relaxation methods. These may not help your speech, but being able to relax can often make learning more effective, and it is enjoyable.

· *Being a Parent who Stammers* ·

If you are a parent who stammers, you may be worried that you will produce children who stammer or you may already have a stammering child. Although it is thought that stammering, in some cases, can have a genetic cause, it does not mean that because you stammer your children are bound to do so as well. But you know that stammering may exist in the family gene pool. We all carry genetic predispositions that we would rather were not there and most of us are usually unaware of much of our genetic inheritance. No one can guarantee to pass on only 'good' genes to their offspring and, fortunately, only a small minority of people see that as a desirable scenario anyway.

Some parents who stammer worry that their children are going to stammer as a result of imitating their speech. Children do imitate their parents in the way they walk, talk and general mannerisms. However, it is not the case that children become stammerers by imitating a parent who stammers.

Try to bear in mind that stammering is just one part of you; your child will relate to you as a whole human being, not just to your speech. You should not regard yourself primarily as a person who stammers, because your child certainly won't. He or she may see you as short, tall or of average height, serious, light-hearted or a bit of each, easygoing, strict or sometimes both, *and* as somebody who stammers. There is so much about you that your child will get to know; your speech will just be a part of it.

If your child is beginning to show signs of stammering, try not to become over-anxious. As we have seen, when young children first learn to speak they can go through quite a long period of dysfluency. It does not mean that they are going to become stammerers, but the longer these periods are, the more likely it is that the stammer will persist.

As a stammerer yourself you may become especially concerned about your child's speech. This is understandable. However, if you convey your anxiety to your child, it will put pressure on him or her to speak more fluently to please you. These kinds of message can be given unintentionally through non-verbal communication, which children are very good at picking up.

In some ways, you are better equipped than a fluent parent to prevent a child who is a potential stammerer from becoming one. You know what to do and what not to do. You know not to make demands on his or her speech; not to ask him to speak more clearly, quickly or grammatically, and not to interrupt. You know not to ask him to perform if he doesn't want to, or to ask too many questions. You also know how important it is to give him plenty of time to speak and not to finish his sentences for him. You know the main issues that are involved. Non-stammering parents may not discover these things until the child is older and the stammering is more established.

On the other hand, you also know that early intervention can be very successful. So if you are concerned that your child may be stammering, take him or her to a speech and language therapist for an expert opinion. Your doctor can refer you to one, or if you contact The British Stammering Association, they can give you the names of therapists in your area.

If your child continues to be dysfluent, there is a lot you can do in providing support, understanding as well as information to help him or her to speak more fluently or more freely. More than that, you can provide your child with an empathy that is not easily obtainable elsewhere. You have been there yourself, and maybe still are there, and you know how it feels.

You may be the person with whom your child can practise speech techniques. You may also be the one he can talk to about his feelings, his fears and expectations. If you can encourage your child to open up to you and discuss things with you as a matter of course, knowing that he will experience patience and understanding, the chances are that he will not hide behind a wall of comparative silence as so many people who stammer do. He will have experienced at least one ongoing dialogue. By keeping in such close touch with your stammering child, you are not only likely to be aware of the emotional problems as they arise, but you may also be able to pick up on speech patterns that keep the stammering in place. For example, you will probably notice when he is avoiding certain words or reconstructing his sentences and can possibly encourage him to stop it.

Sometimes it is difficult to help someone who shares the same problems as we do, particularly if the person is our own son or daughter. It seems extraordinary, because we should know what it is they are going through; however, we can be very impatient with them.

You may have come across the person who says something like: 'I can't stand Philip. He is so short-tempered and snappy. He really should learn to give people a chance.' Your mouth drops open, because the terms 'short-tempered' and 'snappy' are the ones that you associate with the speaker, perhaps even more so than with Philip.

What happens is that sometimes when we hate something about ourselves we disassociate from it. It doesn't belong to us. We either try to forget about it, don't talk about it or project it on to someone else. In his heart of hearts the speaker knows that he is short-tempered and snappy, but he is so unhappy about it that he doesn't admit it, even to himself. Since he doesn't own up to his failings, he can't be angry with himself for being snappy and short-tempered, so he is especially angry with Philip instead.

You may dislike your stammer, but the fact that you stammer can be a great benefit to your stammering child if you choose to view and use it that way. If you can accept that stammering is part of you, you will be able to accept very much more easily that it is just a part of him. You can then move on to helping him improve his speaking in whichever way he wants. You may find that it also helps you.

· *Family Life* ·

Stammering can affect family life in several ways, particularly if the person who stammers is practising avoidance behaviour. His or her partner may shoulder the responsibility for anything that requires speech and handle all the confrontational issues that arise. These can include day-to-day dialogue in shops, with tradesmen and bank managers, for example. Conflicts and problems that occur with children, relatives and friends may also be the sole domain of the stammerer's spouse. It can place a heavy burden on the partner who is constantly having to complain and enforce discipline.

Elizabeth says in the family story later in the chapter: 'I found it a bit too much and I can't say I relished it.' When you read her story, you will see that Elizabeth regrets the time and opportunities she and her stammering partner, Julian, missed. They didn't do all the things they could have done. Simple, everyday things like going out more, taking holidays and moving house. She feels that Julian's stammer got in the way of a more active and fulfilling life.

For his part, Julian says that when his children were young he was a distant figure. His wife did most of the communicating with them and although this did not adversely affect them in any way, Julian wishes he had found his voice (so to speak) earlier, while the family was still young and the children were still at home.

If stammering is an issue that you cannot confront at the moment, there are less verbal ways in which you can relate to your children and show them that you love them and are there for them. Making time for hobbies like drawing, painting and woodwork, and taking part in activities like football, tennis and swimming are some of the many ways in which you can be with your children without having to talk very much. Young children adapt very easily and fit in with people's difficulties and idiosyncrasies. If you enjoy being with them they will be happy to be with you and you may well find that you are able to speak more fluently to your children than you can to anyone else.

Julian says that although his wife was very supportive, he avoided talking about stammering. Elizabeth comments that it was not swept under the carpet and that at times she brought up the issue of therapy. Julian was much more fluent when speaking to her than he was with other people. None the less, stammering was a subject that he avoided, possibly because it was too painful. When Julian finally did go for speech therapy and became a much more confident speaker, the family dynamics changed. He answered the telephone and took over the decision-making and Elizabeth found herself taking a welcome back seat.

This period of readjustment can be difficult. After years of being in charge of all the major decisions, it can be difficult to hand over the reins. You get used to being one kind of person and then you have to become someone else. Along with the pride and elation that result when the partner who stammers gets to grips with his problem and starts metamorphosing into a more dominant, maybe even dynamic, individual, comes the question of adapting to the new relationship. Some partners must ask themselves: 'When he was passive I was active. Now that he is active, do I have to be passive?' Some people may enjoy the role reversal but others may prefer some kind of negotiation.

· *Julian* ·

Julian, who has two grown-up children, has stammered all his life. It was never spoken about at home by his parents or at school by his teachers. This reticence to speak about stammering was carried on by Julian in adult life. He was very reluctant to talk about it with his wife, Elizabeth, despite the fact that she was very supportive. However, in his early forties Julian sought help for his stammer. First, he saw a speech and language therapist on his own and then went on three intensive speech therapy courses.

I have always stammered, ever since I can remember. I can remember stammering at school and I think it was the start of it making me introverted. I chose not to speak to people because I found it hard. I became a bit of a loner at school. I had two or three close friends, but I never actually pushed myself to take part in things. I couldn't speak to the opposite sex. Unless I was specifically asked to, I never spoke in class, assemblies or discussion groups at all because of the overwhelming fear of stammering and looking a complete idiot.

I don't remember any teasing, but I often think that I blocked that out mentally. I can recall two or three teachers who found it quite amusing to make me stand up and read a passage orally. At the time teachers were all-powerful and everybody had to do as they were told. At school I was only ever interested in English Language and Literature and, up to a point, I hid behind that and spent endless hours reading.

I chose to be isolated at school. My stammering was never talked about at school. It wasn't ever talked about at home either. I think my parents thought I'd grow out of it. It was all swept under the carpet, really. My two younger siblings didn't stammer at all and there is no history of it in the family.

As a teenager, I had a terrible stammer with head-jerking, facial tics and everything else which generally now I have under control. But as a teenager, without any experience of speech therapy, it wasn't under control at all. It was extremely embarrassing and frustrating and I just didn't know which way to turn . . . . I'd never even heard of speech therapy then.

I think at the point I left school I hadn't a clue what I wanted to do. I had no qualifications other than an O level in English Language. My mother saw a job advertised which she thought was right for me. I applied for the position and got the interview and, to my shame, she came with me. I was 16 at the time and, as I recall, she did all the talking.

In later years I was quite angry about that, but because I was so introverted I think I was quite pleased that she came at the time. I am ashamed to say that now. If I had been helped as a child or as a teenager, I might have been more aware and been able to create and control the situation myself without my mother having to do it.

I was offered the job anyway and I'm still there 38 years later. Over the years I have been promoted several times and I am now in quite a responsible position.

For many years I did not have to talk to people in my job. I never had to answer the telephone. I was checking invoices and packing and putting away stock. I didn't have to communicate with people very much. But as time went by I was given more and more responsibility and it meant that I had to answer the telephone and attend meetings with people I didn't know and had never met before.

It was an endless problem for me at first. I had no idea how to control my speech and I would be stammering away and often when I was talking on the telephone people would say: 'It sounds as if we've got a fault on the line.' I couldn't explain to them that I had a stammer and it wasn't a fault on the line, it was me.

In 1985 I had the flu and before returning to work I had to go and see my GP. While I was in the surgery I found myself telling my doctor that I had a stammer and was wondering if anything could be done for me. He said he could arrange for me to see a speech therapist. I walked out of the surgery shaking. I was terrified, wondering what I had done, because despite the fact that I stammered, I was in this introverted cosy little world. I realised that, having asked for this appointment, I was going to have to come out of that and face the problem. That was awesome for me.

When the appointment came through I can remember going through absolute agony wondering how I was going to ask my boss for time off. Would I be able to find my way to the therapist? And would I be able to speak to her if and when I got there? However, within about 10 minutes of my being there I realised that I should have done this years ago. I can recall the therapist saying that she couldn't cure my stammer but she could show me how to control it. She showed me the slow prolonged speech technique. It was a gradual programme of improvement. But after that I was able to control my speech up to a point and if I was talking to new people I could explain that I stammered, which instantly eased the situation.

After the initial speech therapy I started to improve slowly in confidence and self-esteem. I was able to talk to colleagues at work and, more importantly, to my wife and sons. Until then stammering wasn't really talked about at home because I chose not to, even though my wife was extremely supportive and had always encouraged me to talk about it. Now it was so much easier.

Elizabeth and I met through working in the same firm. One of my colleagues who knew the two of us quite well acted as a go-between. I just couldn't bring myself initially to speak to Elizabeth. I would send her letters and this third party carried messages between us. I asked Elizabeth for a date by letter and we went to the pictures. I would see her occasionally at lunch-time and we would go for a stroll in a nearby park. Slowly but surely we started to talk and we became closer then. Inside 12 months we were engaged. My speech didn't seem to bother her at all.

With many stammerers, improving speech also improves their confidence. In times past their partner may have made the decisions for everything and answered every telephone call. With the new-found confidence the stammerer suddenly wants to answer the telephone and make the decisions and they can perhaps go over the top and create extra problems for their partner. I have had to be conscious of the fact that I don't have to answer every telephone call and make every decision and that the two of us are doing this as a couple.

Stammering can make you feel very isolated in the family. It can be a question of not taking any sort of lead in anything and not really even speaking unless you're spoken to. When my sons were young I felt I was a distant figure. It was Elizabeth they turned to mainly with problems at school. It is hard to bridge that gap without speech. People who stammer have to break through that if they possibly can, particularly in family situations. It is so important to communicate with your family. You only have one chance at it, after all.

· *Elizabeth* ·

It was not too bad when we first got married and there were just the two of us. The problems arose when we had a family and he always took a back seat. I found that very frustrating. He wouldn't answer the phone or the door. We never had a row about it but sometimes I wished that he would become a bit more forthcoming.

Speaking was never a big issue in our house. As far as the children were concerned, he was a stammerer when they were born and they just accepted it. We never swept the stammering under the carpet, but Julian never wanted an argument about anything. If there was any kind of confrontation with anyone, I would have to do it and I didn't like it very much.

We did communicate, but he would walk away from an argument, which is very frustrating. I would have wanted him to stay in there. I think it would have been far better for him to get his point over. That is what he has done with a lot of his life – walk away. But Julian has never had a chip on his shoulder about his stammer.

I wish he had had speech therapy years ago. It has made such a difference. I think we would have both been more outgoing. When we were first married, he would often read aloud and it was so frustrating because he would hardly ever stammer when it was just the two of us. We used to talk about it and we did try to do something, but the only thing offered to us was therapy in a psychiatric unit at our local hospital. It was called regression therapy. They gave him drugs which put him under hypnosis. I was there with him. They tried to take him back to the point where the stammer started.

It made him very talkative and occasionally hallucinogenic. He went back to the time when he was at school. They were trying to pinpoint anything that might have brought on his stammer. He did not talk in a child's voice like they show on films. But it wasn't normal speech either. He really slowed down and did not stammer to a great extent. He would recall things in his childhood, but he never got to the point where the stammer started.

Sometimes Julian's stammering has stood in the way socially for us as a couple. In restaurants I used to hate it when I had to order, and I always had to order. But I don't have to any more. I think to a degree that put me off eating out. We did go, but not as much as maybe we should have done. It was the same with booking tickets. When there was a crowd of us it eased the situation, but he was never very forthcoming. He was never the centre of attention and he would never start a conversation. That made it awkward for me sometimes. It was hard work.

Neither of my children stammer. We thought at one point that they might. I always felt that if either one of them ever gave the slightest signs of picking up a stammer I would be on my GP's doorstep. I felt so strongly about it as I knew what my husband had been through. Thankfully, it didn't happen.

I remember years ago I really did let it get to me and when I wanted to blame something I would blame his lack of motivation due to his stammer. There were times in our marriage when I could have walked away. It was so restricting. Julian's restrictions restricted me, but I got over it. We've now been married 32 years.

It was when the boys were younger that we really had our problems. To have a part-time job and look after the children as well as the house was hard work. Julian was no help, because he had got into this attitude that he had a stammer and couldn't do things. It was very frustrating.

When I was stuck at home all day, I was waiting for someone to come home and give me some motivation and say things like 'Let's move house, let's get a new job, let's go on holiday, let's be normal.' Things like that never occurred to Julian. His thinking was: 'I've got a stammer. I can't do that.'

Now that he's had therapy I think it's a bit of role reversal, really. I tend to take a back seat and let him get on with it. It has had some effect on me now that he is much better. I think I was always lacking in confidence and the fact that I had to make decisions forced me into it. In fact I think some of my confidence might have gone since Julian has become more confident. Overall, though, I have great pride in the strides that he has made.

· *Robin* ·

Robin has a PhD in nutrition. He has had a highly successful career, mainly as a lecturer. Talking in public has always been difficult for him and in the early days of teaching he found it extremely nerve-racking. However, over a period of time he was able to control both his stammer and his nerves to such an extent that he even stood for

Parliament. Although he never became an MP, Robin is now a councillor in the Purbeck District of Poole, where, needless to say, he is continually expected to talk in front of audiences. Here is his story:

I started stammering pretty soon after I started talking which I think was when I was about two years old. There are various theories as to why this may have been. One was that my mother and my aunt used to talk incessantly and I could never get a word in edgeways. I suppose in a nice Jewish family this is only to be expected!

I was the second child in the family, but my elder brother was 12 years older than I was. He was more like an uncle. In my parents' eyes my brother was perfect and it was very apparent early on that I was not. Although he enjoyed playing with me and was a very nice older brother, I know I was not the boy companion he would liked to have had. The age gap was too big. Also, he was away in boarding school most of the time.

When I was about two something else happened. I was running up to the front door. I fell over and I bashed my lip. It was during the war. I was taken into hospital and they patched me up and put stitches in my lip without an anaesthetic. Apparently my stammer became much worse after that.

I was slow at learning to read, which did nothing for my self-confidence, but added to that I had difficulty reading aloud in class because of my stammer. I had a repetitive stammer at that stage. I would repeat the same words or the same syllable.

Fortunately, I was very good at maths. I came from a family with high expectations. My mother's ideal was a son who would read English at Oxford. I was not the sort of son who could do that.

My mother was always late for everything. She used to get me to school late when I was in primary school, which I used to find terrible. I was very nervous about that and I was always being told off by the teachers.

My parents had this wonderful theory that it was very good for boys to go to boarding school. They keyed me up for this and at seven and a half I was sent off to a prep school in Bognor Regis. The whole idea of having a child and sending him away almost as soon as he can walk is, to my mind, ridiculous. I suppose I never fully came to terms with that. I don't think that the school was particularly strict but it is significant that in my first term there I got beaten with a hairbrush about eight times or more for such misdemeanours as talking when lights were out in the dormitory. I didn't do anything drastically bad.

All the other children at school who had their birthdays during term-time would be sent a cake or something from home. My mother would never get anything done on time. It made me as sick as a dog. I'd get very upset.

I think my stammering got worse. At the age of eight and a half I wrote to my mother saying that I didn't like boarding school and I would like to go home. It seemed to me that she took no notice of this letter. I subsequently found out that my parents may have made some efforts to find me a preparatory school in London, but they were all full. I knew that there were other children who had been at school and had gone back home and this is what I wanted to do. But it didn't happen. I stayed there until I was 13 years old and then I went to Stowe [a public school].

Although I was reasonably competent from the academic point of view and good at a variety of sports like swimming, running, hurdling, athletics and so on, I had very little confidence in public because of my stammer.

After I got to Stowe and as I got older, I used to try and put myself in situations where I would have to speak properly for certain things. For instance, when I was in the Combined Cadet Corps at school I soon became a lance corporal because I was good at getting things done. I was quickly promoted to sergeant. In this post I had to issue people with instructions and orders. I was extremely anxious and I tended to block, but I was able to do what was required and it gave me a certain amount of confidence. I have always been an ambitious person, but I must admit that I never spoke in the debating society at school because I was too nervous to do that.

After school I went to university, which I enjoyed far more. I didn't say too much in public at that stage, but my social life improved. I played bridge much more seriously, and tennis, and I did not have too many problems speaking socially, although if there was ever a woman I really liked I found that I couldn't talk to her. This may not have been just to do with the stammer. I think it was a lack of self-confidence with women through going to a male-only school.

After I had finished my BSc I got a post in Cambridge doing research. As I had an industrially financed post, I had to go around the poultry industry and I had to telephone all sorts of people. After I got into it I was all right. My technique on the phone improved considerably. I am sure I used all the avoidances that stammerers do. I would turn sentences around so that I didn't have to make an explosive noise like a P or a B.

When I decided to take my PhD, I got an Inner London Authority research award and in order to earn extra money I did some part-time teaching. It came in two forms. The first was easy. It was demonstrating things to science students and all I had to do was to say things like 'Don't set fire to that' or 'Be careful with that or it will explode,' which was not difficult. But then I was offered some part-time teaching at Westminster College and I had to lecture in nutrition to catering students. I found that much more difficult, but I did do it. I spent ages researching, but my delivery was not good.

When I was in my mid-twenties I had speech therapy, which helped a little. I can remember speaking slowly in a monosyllabic way. It didn't sound like normal speech. I sounded like an automaton. We also did shadow reading, where the speech therapist reads a little bit ahead of you so she says the syllables slightly before you do. It gets you used to saying difficult sounds like Ps and Bs. I think that helped a bit.

I was then given the opportunity to teach the nutrition part of the BSc course in food science at a university. I used to work very hard to ensure that the students were getting everything they needed and I would prepare long and detailed handouts to give them. I found one way of coping. I put the sentences that I wanted to give out on an overhead acetate and I didn't look at the students, just at the acetate, while I was attempting to read it or talk to it. This worked quite well. I used similar techniques when lecturing to learned societies.

In 1974 I stood for Parliament. I had to give some speeches in public then and I was extremely nervous. However, people who stand for candidacy in seats they cannot possibly win are in a very fortunate position, insofar as nobody listens to a thing they say! None the less I got 20 per cent of the votes and my deposit back.

I am much more relaxed now than I used to be and I have more self-confidence, and that helps my speech. I do have to speak in Council meetings now. I find having to chair meetings difficult, but the Purbeck District Councillors are all very tolerant and on the occasions that I do stand up and spout nobody heckles me.

7

IN THE WORKPLACE

Some of the most successful people in the world are stammerers. Not only do they come from all walks of life, but the jobs that they do so well cover a very wide range. Yet, despite the enormous success that some people who stammer achieve, the workplace is one of the major environments where other stammerers feel restricted and limited by their dysfluency.

The job we do has an extremely significant bearing on our lives and it is not just in terms of how much money we earn. Enjoying the work and knowing that we do it well gives us all a strong feeling of self-worth. Conversely, it can be very undermining and frustrating to feel that we are in a job that is below our capabilities. The feeling of self-esteem we gain in the workplace can affect all the other areas of our lives.

Someone who likes his job and feels fulfilled by it is more likely to enjoy other aspects of his life than is someone who feels dissatisfied. When you consider how long each of us spends at work, it is not surprising that the workplace has such a strong influence on our well-being.

At a recent Open Day of The British Stammering Association, one young man told fellow stammerers that they should have the confidence, determination and self-belief to do the jobs and pursue the careers that they really wanted to do. They should not go for the easy options and the jobs that don't require much speaking, but aim for those they wanted.

Research has shown that people who stammer tend to select vocations with their dysfluency in mind. They also experience discrimination in the workplace and often work in positions below their capability. Managers and colleagues don't always understand the problems that people who stammer experience at work. Talking at meetings and making presentations are two of the situations that many stammerers fear most.

People who stammer often undervalue themselves because they believe that their managers and colleagues think they are less able than non-stammerers. However, a recent project undertaken in the workplace by two speech and language therapists, Anne Ayre and Louise Wright, found that this is not always the case. The study, which is outlined in greater detail below, revealed that, whereas some workers who stammer believe that they are not held in high regard by their workmates, the reality is that they are greatly respected. The problem is that there is often little or no communication. The person who stammers probably never talks about his problems or initiates any dialogue; nor does he receive much feedback. If he did, the chances are that he would be very pleasantly surprised!

· *The British Aerospace Project* ·

A therapy programme for people who stammer, funded by British Aerospace, Military Aircraft, was carried out in the company's workplace by Louise Wright and Anne Ayre. Seven dysfluent employees took part in a group therapy course and for each a nominated colleague and manager was also involved. So seven distinct threesomes were created, providing a sample for the study.

The course itself consisted of weekly therapy sessions of three hours for 12 weeks, during work time and on site. Weekly assignments to transfer skills were carried out in the workplace. The stammerers were encouraged to enlist the support of their colleague and the latter attended one social meeting and one therapy meeting, where they actively took part in group discussions. The managers joined the therapists for two group discussions over a working lunch, each lasting an hour and a half. Here they shared experiences generated by the therapy programme. Towards the end of the course each threesome attended a meeting with one of the therapists, who facilitated discussion about the person's stammer and its impact at work. Strategies to combat the problems were negotiated.

Qualitative data designed to establish the attitudes and experiences of the groups were gathered immediately before, shortly after and seven months after the programme.

Contribution to meetings was a key theme in this project, as it is in the workplace generally these days. As Ayre and Wright observe in their study:

> This means that effective performance, that is, contributing fully, in meetings is seen as being very important. For the delegates (stammerers) meetings were situations where much anxiety and avoidance occurred. It became apparent, however, that the

managers' and colleagues' perceptions of the impact of the stammer on performance in meetings, and the accompanying stress, varied from complete ignorance to considerable awareness.

One manager correctly assessed that his employee struggled in group scenarios and he rightly put this down to the stammerer's need to sound polished and professional. This put him under pressure and made the stammer worse.

Other managers felt that their employees had no fear of speaking in meetings, but when questioned the stammerers themselves said that they kept quiet at meetings, preferring to buttonhole their bosses when they were on their own. Others hid their light under a bushel by not contributing and not admitting to having the knowledge that they had.

After the course the stammerers felt much more able to participate at meetings. One who was still experiencing difficulty wrote a list of the points that he wanted to make which he kept between himself and his manager. This way he had the option of making the points out loud if he was able to, but if he was not, his manager could help him out until his confidence increased.

What came out of the triad discussions with the therapist was that it helped the person who stammered if a manager and at least one colleague understood his problems and was sympathetic to them. This openness improved communication as much as learning the actual speech techniques did. For their part, the managers and colleagues said that it was important to have an input from their workmates who stammered. 'What he has to say generally is of benefit to the whole group,' was the comment of one manager.

Other people's opinion proved to be an area where there were intrinsic misconceptions. Stammerers who believed that they were seen as being stupid were described by managers and colleagues as 'bright'. One stammerer who went to great pains to avoid his manager, because he was convinced that the man had a very poor opinion of him, was surprised to discover that his manager thought him very able.

Openness about stammering is a key issue with stammerers in many situations, including in the workplace. During the course, managers and colleagues were able to say how difficult it was for them to broach the subject of stammering because of their fear of causing distress. Stammerers explained how difficult and sometimes frightening it was to talk about stammering. However, after the course, managers and colleagues remarked that it was much easier to deal with something that was out in the open. The stammerers observed that the openness took off the pressure and brought down the barriers.

Commenting on what they had learnt from the project, Ayre and Wright said: 'Raising awareness and being open about stuttering at work can change attitudes and behaviours resulting in more positive experiences for everyone.'

Bearing in mind the points raised by this project, let us look at some of the issues surrounding stammering and work in general.

· *Job Interviews* ·

People who stammer have cited interviews as one of life's biggest bugbears. So much can depend on your ability to sell yourself at an interview that many non-stammerers attend them quaking in their shoes. It is, of course, much more nerve-racking for those who are dysfluent. Stress and nervousness can make the stammer so much worse and even people who only stammer occasionally have said that they inevitably stammer at interviews. So what should you do?

Be open

Perhaps one of the most important things you need to get across at an interview is that your stammer is only a part of you, just like your height and weight and the colour of your eyes. It may slow you down a little in talking situations, but it may not. In any event, it is not going to interfere with your ability to do the job.

The people who interview you are not going to know all this unless you tell them. They may have difficulty in broaching the subject at all unless you introduce it. As many stammerers have said and the British Aerospace study found, bringing the issue out into the open can reduce stammering. You are less likely to stammer badly if you talk about it in the interview than if you try to hide it.

Louise Wright suggests that people who stammer might like to say something along these lines:

You've noticed that I'm stammering. I'd like to point out that I'm stammering at my worst here because I'm nervous, like everybody is at an interview. Most of the time it is not nearly so severe and I can manage it. And it doesn't stop me from doing anything that I want to do. Sometimes it takes me a little longer to say things, but I think that my other qualities far outweigh that.

And then start talking about your qualities. By taking the bull by the horns in this way, you are taking control of your speech and, to some extent, of the interview.

Be prepared

Non-stammerers can go to a great deal of trouble in preparing for an interview. They will think about what they are going to wear, the state of their hair and the cleanliness of their nails. Many will have also spent some time in the library researching the company for which they wish to work. They will have thought about what they are going to say, how to describe their strengths and their weaknesses. They will think about the kinds of question they may be asked and how they should reply to show themselves in the best light.

Some people who stammer are so worried about their dysfluency that they focus only on their stammer. They forget to do the basic things that are important for a successful interview. However, it is perhaps even more important for someone who stammers to go for an interview well prepared. It will give you some much-needed confidence and confirm to your would-be employers that you are intelligent and capable and that your dysfluency is just a small part of you.

Non-verbal communication

Remember that communication is not only about speech. Maintaining soft eye contact is very important. Don't look away or down at the floor if you start to stammer. Keep the connection by looking at the person or people who are interviewing you. If you look away, the non-verbal message is 'I'm embarrassed about stammering.' This is likely to embarrass the listener. If you maintain eye contact you are saying: 'I stammer, but it's okay,' which is a much more relaxing message to give.

Body language is also important. If you sit on the edge of your seat, all tensed up, you will give the impression of being very nervous. If you slouch into the chair with your body pointed towards the door you will seem uninterested. Try to relax into the chair as best you can and make sure that your body is facing towards the interviewer. If you can manage a smile too, so much the better.

Listen

When we are nervous, one of the most difficult things to do is to concentrate on what the other person is saying. But it is worth a try, and even if you cannot take in everything that is being said, it is good at least to give the impression that you are listening. So remember to wait your turn to speak. It is very tempting when you feel you are on a fluent roll to keep talking, but that does not always make for effective communication. Instead, let the other person speak, listen to the questions and answer them to the best of your ability, even if you stammer. The interviewer may be far more interested in your qualifications, work experience and capabilities than in your speech.

· *Speaking Out at Work* ·

Some of the most significant findings of the project at British Aerospace involved hiding the stammer at work. People who stammer often keep themselves trapped in a secret world at work. They may be so fearful of being discovered to be a stammerer or considered less able than their more fluent colleagues that they do not take part in all the aspects of working life. Their bosses and workmates don't find out what they are really like and so everybody misses out.

Giving permission

It is very difficult for anyone other than the person who stammers to bring up the issue of stammering. People generally don't want to be tactless or offensive, so the cue has to come from you. There is so much anxiety and even fear attached to stammering that it is not easy to be open about it. This can place quite a heavy burden on the stammerer to take the responsibility for bringing up the subject.

As with anything else, this is best done in easy stages. If you have a colleague or a manager who seems sensitive and sympathetic, you can start by telling him or her. You don't have to give your life story. All you have to do is to say that you have a stammer. If you can do this in the context of something specific, you may find it easier. It may be, for instance, that you find talking on the phone makes you stammer more because, like Bob in Chapter Twelve, you are conscious that other people are listening. Try confiding in your colleague. You could say something like 'I'm struggling with my stammer on the phone today.'

Your colleague's response may be that he or she hasn't noticed. You can then go on to mention the situations in which you become more dysfluent, and explain how you try to manage your stammer. However, *don't be tempted to allow your sympathetic colleague to take over talking on the telephone for you*. The idea is to do more talking, not less!

Once you have started talking about stammering to one colleague, you may find it easier to bring it more and more out into the open, until it is no longer a taboo subject.

Often the closest friendships are forged at work, because you see so much of your colleagues. Work isn't always a competitive situation; it can sometimes be mutually supportive. It is a shame to miss out on making good friends and having some fun just because you stammer. Sympathetic colleagues are sometimes the ideal people with whom to practise speech techniques. They see you every day, they know you and, if they are aware that you are working on your stammer, they may be quite happy to spend a coffee break or lunch hour working on your speech with you.

Feedback

How can you possibly know how you are regarded at work if you don't enter into any dialogue? In the project conducted by Louise Wright and Anne Ayre, it transpired that one of the stammerers who believed everyone thought he was awful was actually considered to be the brightest man there by both his manager and his colleague. Had the question of his stammer not been aired and had there been no discussion, how would he ever have discovered that?

Louise Wright comments:

Often when people have stammered from childhood, their self-esteem has been affected in a negative way. If they've had bad experiences at school they may have experienced negative feedback and have bad memories. They may have grown up believing that they are not as good as other people and not able to do things as well as others. This belief is perpetuated when they are in a work situation, despite the esteem that their managers and colleagues may hold them in.

A person who is told by his boss or his colleagues that he does his job well is going to feel validated. To be told that you are good at what you do does wonders for your self-esteem. One of the most effective ways of overcoming some of the problems of stammering is to gain confidence in yourself. Everyone interviewed for this book was agreed on this point, whether they were people who stammered, therapists, partners or friends. Bring increased self-confidence into the equation and you have a person who speaks more fluently or stammers more fluently – either way, he or she is participating just as fully as everyone else, in whatever sphere of life.

A very important point to bear in mind is that the company who employs you presumably does so because they need your skills. People who pretend to know less than they do to get out of speaking situations can sometimes be frustrating to work with. Colleagues and managers may be well aware that the person has a great deal to contribute, but they may find it very difficult to access that knowledge and expertise, particularly in group situations.

Therefore, if you avoid speaking, you may not only conceal your true value from the people you work with, but deny them your full collaboration and support.

Meetings and presentations

Meetings can create the most problems for people who stammer. Presentations may not be quite so bad. Some people find that when they stand up at the front and are in control, with no one interrupting them, they have little difficulty in speaking. There are many lecturers who stammer, as well as actors and other people working in the media, and it seems that being in control, having a script or playing a part damps down the stammer.

Meetings can be nerve-racking, even for non-stammerers. It is often hard to get your point across without interrupting and before the next person speaks, especially in a talkative group. As we saw earlier, one of the people in the British Aerospace project made a list of the things he wanted to say. This reassured him that, one way or another, his contribution would be made. It meant that his employer was not going to miss out, either.

If stammering is out in the open and not a taboo subject, fail-safe measures like this can be taken if necessary. Obviously, it is best to join in the meeting if you can. If your colleagues are aware that you stammer, you may find that when you start to speak they will give you more time than they give each other. The more that is known about stammering, the more this is likely to be the case. If people realise that starting a sentence is the difficult bit for you, they will probably remember to give you a chance to begin. Most of us can be quite sensitive to each other's needs, but only if we are put in the picture.

What next?

One of the fears of becoming more outgoing is the question of where it will lead. People who have led restricted lives because of their dysfluency, always playing it safe, may be understandably fearful of experimenting with new situations. If you start speaking to your manager and contributing at meetings, he may decide that you are more than capable of doing your present job. He may suggest that you improve your career prospects by attending a management training course or a presentations skills course, for example. New doors may open, new experiences may be offered, but are you ready for them?

You may or may not be prepared to make progress, but what you can do is to talk about it. It may be that you need a little time to acquire more self-confidence, or you may be half-way there already but just need a little push. Alternatively, you may not want to change what you do. All these are valid points which you can make should an opportunity for changes be presented.

· *Therapy* ·

Some very significant progress was made by the workers who stammered in the British Aerospace project. Louise Wright explains how this was achieved:

> Our aim in therapy was first of all to get people to have more of a sense of control over their stammering. This doesn't necessarily mean being more fluent, but knowing how it works.
>
> The first thing we got them to do was to analyse their stammering and look at how non-stammerers speak. So they started to look at their speech and take it to bits. Then we worked on getting them to think how they could communicate more effectively.
>
> Some needed to slow their rate down. Others needed to stop struggling against the stammer and just let it flow out. That actually made the stammers a lot easier and a lot smaller. Some of them were using all sorts of odd tricks to try and cover up their stammer which made them sound strange. They would put in words like 'well', 'er', 'you know' and a lot of preamble to disguise the fact that they couldn't say something like their name. When they started to discard all this and go for the words that they wanted to say, they realised that they sounded much clearer and were so much better communicators and that people responded better.
>
> So they started to get a feel that they could change the way they spoke and communicate better. They saw themselves on video and they got feedback from each other.

But it was not just what we did with their speech but also the psychological changes that needed to be made. Reducing their problems with low self-esteem was important. When we were able to get them to talk to their colleagues and managers, they started to get positive feedback. If it is the first time that your manager says to you that you're actually the best one on the shop floor, you will start to think differently about yourself and put your stammer into perspective. When he says that he is not bothered about your speech, but it's the fact that you know more about the job than anyone else that he is giving you all these apprentices, you get a truer feeling of your worth.

The therapy was a combination of what we did with their speech and what we got them to do within the workplace. It was working on both parts of the stammering iceberg: above the surface and below it.

For various reasons including size, finance and commitment, not many organisations would be able to fund the kind of therapy course that was undertaken at British Aerospace. So, generally speaking, it is not likely that therapy will take place on site as it did in this project.

Speech and language therapists work with families and with teachers. Going into the workplace to talk to managers is not beyond the skills of the therapists, but at present it is not always possible to do it on the NHS because of the time involved. But there is no reason why an interested manager cannot attend an individual speech therapy session with his or her employee who stammers.

If you would like to raise awareness of stammering in your work situation, you can get some relevant leaflets from The British Stammering Association to give to your manager or colleagues. If you are going for speech therapy and would like your therapist to speak to your manager, he or she will probably be quite happy to do this, at least on the phone.

· *Disability Discrimination Act 1995* ·

This Act brings in new laws aimed at ending the discrimination which many disabled people face. It places some responsibility on the employer to make reasonable adjustments to accommodate the needs of disabled employees. If they see that somebody has a problem or is having difficulties, they must provide him or her with opportunities to discuss these issues in confidence.

The Act gives new rights to people who have a disability which makes it difficult to carry out their normal day-to-day activities. The disability must be substantial and have a long-term effect. Stammering is named in the Act as a possible disability. An employer may not treat any employee less favourably than the rest because of his or her disability without good reason.

Disabled people who feel that they have been discriminated against at work will be able to complain to an industrial tribunal. They will no longer need to register as disabled and employers will no longer be required to employ a quota of registered disabled people.

The employment part of the Act does not apply to employers who employ fewer than 20 people, but they will still be encouraged to follow good practice guidelines. Nor does it apply to operational staff employed in the armed forces, police, prison and fire services or to anyone employed on ships, hovercrafts or aeroplanes.

· *David* ·

David is a Sergeant in the Royal Air Force. For some time he has worked as an air traffic controller. He has stammered since he was six years old.

When I was young I experienced being the butt of jokes, mickey-taking and bullying. People would think that there was something wrong with me so I must be an easy target. But I never had a problem with schoolwork unless I had to talk aloud or was asked a question and I stammered over the reply. I'd get nervous, go red and I was very conscious of the fact that I had stammered. The average schoolboy or girl would laugh.

It wasn't until I joined the Air Force that I started to do anything about my speech. My parents thought that my stammer would die out. I had a teacher I was petrified of and they thought that once I got out of her class my stammer would go. Unfortunately, it didn't. But I was a moderate stammerer, not a severe one.

In 1985 my admin. sergeant asked what I wanted to do with my career. I said I wanted to do air traffic control and he said I'd better get my stammer checked. I hadn't even thought about it. I'd pushed it to the back of my mind. The joking had gone. I was now with mature people.

I went into hospital in Lincoln and I spent 10 days there. It was mainly relaxation. They monitored me and said that the only thing I was slightly over the line with was stress. They couldn't find any exterior cause for my stammer.

They gave me relaxation tapes and said that if I was getting stressed I should take time out and listen to these tapes. I thought it was a wasted week. I didn't feel that I got anything out of it whatsoever. But they said that they didn't think my stammer would cause me any problems.

As the years went by I found that I could improve my stammer by trying to speak more slowly. Ann and I have both been married before. In my previous marriage there were many stressful situations. There were lots of things that didn't help my stammer. I feel much more relaxed now. Ann and I get on like a house on fire. It has made a big difference to my speech.

I think if I'd first become an officer and gone into air traffic control straight away it might have been more difficult. My stammer was more prominent then. As it is, it has taken me 12 years and during that time I have learnt the job thoroughly. I know the people. I know exactly how things are run and that's half the job done. It helps when you know what you are doing.

At the moment I am not in a normal airfield. I'm on a bombing range. You have to give the exact words. You can't block. There is a set phraseology book which you have to learn. Every year we get checked out to make sure that we are safe: saying the right phrases and safe in our controlling. The guys who check us are from the actual units where we were trained. Their main object is to make sure that we are safe and expeditious in our controlling and that we don't have any near misses. They also make sure that we use 'standard phraseology'.

You have to be on your toes. On a normal airfield it is usually more busy for more of the time than where I am now. I prefer working on an airfield. If you've learnt the phraseology well and you've got all the phrases in your head, and you don't have to think what to say for the announcement it's a big help.

I have problems with words beginning with P. For instance, I can't say 'position' in one full word. I have to cut it in half and say the first bit and then the second bit. The guy on the course said, 'Try swapping the word "position" for "location".' So I use 'location'. It is not exactly the same, but it's OK.

You have to be able to get the word out. You have to say it straight away. If I couldn't do that, I couldn't do the job.

I enjoy my work. I prefer it when I'm on a normal airfield controlling a mixture of aircraft. Not only did we do the fast jets in the military, but we also did everything from a little Cessna 172 up to a Boeing 747 Jumbo. That was really good. On the bombing range we basically get up to four aircraft on to a range and they'll be bombing, using rockets and strafing. They will be dropping everything from a 3 kilo bomb to one of about 2000 lbs. Of course, they are all practice bombs. We control them while they're on the range and get them off it. In the mean time there can be other aircraft that want to come in for one pass and we have to look after them too. We can be controlling up to about 12 aircraft over the range.

It is a totally verbal job and I love it.

· *Nav* ·

Nav is a highly intelligent young man who, despite the fact that he has five A levels, failed to get into medical school because he could not pass the interviews. Nav has since gained a degree in pharmacy and now works as a pharmacist. He has been to speech therapists throughout his childhood and young adulthood for his stammer, without much success. He has also tried hypnotherapy, which did not work for him.

Recently Nav attended the McGuire Institute, which he says has helped him. He has attended some of the intensive courses run by the Institute and has found the back-up help extremely useful. The address of the McGuire Institute appears at the end of the book.

Here is Nav's story:

I started stammering when I started speaking. Parents want to protect their children. If they see a child struggling, they want to help him. I think when my parents saw that I couldn't say things they would say it on my behalf, just to help me and save me embarrassment. Stammering does become a habit and can be used as an excuse for not doing things. If you don't want to do something, you can use your stammer to get someone else to do the task.

Stammering didn't bother me too much as a child. I was OK at school with it. I wasn't very conscious of it there. It was when I had to go for interviews to get into medical school that it became a problem. I wanted to be a doctor and I was confident that I could become one because I had the academic ability.

I went for an interview for a medical degree at King's College in London. There was a panel of five people interviewing me. They asked a couple of questions. I can't remember if I got stuck on the name of my school or on my own name, but I know I blocked. I just could not say it. In those days when I blocked it was like an epileptic fit. From my shoulders upwards I would become so tense that my jaw would lock. My eye contact was non-existent. I did not want to look at the panel because it would have intensified the embarrassment and the pain. I looked down at the floor. At one stage when I did look at the people on the panel I saw that they were looking down at the table. I didn't pass the interview. If you cannot even say your name, what chance have you of getting any job? Even a two-year-old can do that! I didn't pass any interviews for other medical schools either, nor for any other courses.

It seemed to me to be very unfair. I know I can speak, but it is much more difficult in stressful situations. It's like a person sitting a maths exam. Either you can do maths or you can't. If someone can do maths, but in an exam situation he goes to pieces and can't, it doesn't mean that he can't do maths. It just means that he freezes in certain situations. But that is not how the outside world sees it. Just because he may suffer from exam nerves he is condemned. It's a bit like how it is with speaking. I know I can speak fluently when, for instance, I am on my own or with friends, but I have to prove this to the outside world, especially with first impressions. As far as work is concerned, no matter what job you do, you have to be able to talk.

Eventually, because of my five A levels, I was given two unconditional offers to do pharmacy. I didn't have to go through an interview and so I had no difficulty getting in.

While I was still studying I had a pre-registration year working in a pharmacy in a hospital. It was a fairly relaxed job as I did not have to answer the phone or speak to the public very much. I was 'protected' to some extent by my work colleagues. But it doesn't improve your self-esteem.

However, when I got my qualification I had to pull my weight as I was given a relief job on a temporary basis in a new and busier pharmacy. I had to answer the phone and speak to people as anyone else would have to do. It was very good. It changed me. It was so busy that I did not have time to think about how I was going to answer the phone or deal with a customer, I just had to get on and do it. Sometimes people improve if you give them responsibility and don't let them subconsciously hide behind their stammer. And that's what happened to me.

When I opted to be transferred to a less busy pharmacy near home, I went back to being more conscious of making mistakes. I once again started being worried about answering the phone and talking to people. And it becomes a vicious circle. You worry about it, you make a mess, and so you worry even more about it the next time.

I had a lot of speech therapy when I was a child and I went back to it while I was at university. I knew I had to improve my speech to get a job, so I kept on with it. What choice did I have? But the trouble is that if you do something like slow prolonged speech, it is OK while you are within a controlled environment, but once you go out into the real world you can't speak like that because it is impracticable and uncomfortable to implement. So you go back to your natural way of speaking and stammer.

I even found the block-modification techniques didn't really work for me. When I get stuck, it becomes so emotional. I can't stand back from it and produce a technique. It's just not programmable.

I think that there are two things you need in order to succeed. The first is an enormous determination to overcome a chronic stammer and the second is a technique which can be comfortably and practically used in the real world. I had the former, but unfortunately not the latter. What good is a soldier in a battle without any usable weapons?

One day when I was reading the newspaper I saw an article about a stammerer who had been to a McGuire Institute course. He now enjoyed talking so much that he had run himself up an enormous phone bill. I decided to give it a try.

One of the main things I liked about the McGuire Institute was that it is run by stammerers for stammerers. The people teaching were all stammerers, except that now they didn't stammer. They played us video-tapes to show us how they used to speak, because you wouldn't have believed them otherwise. And they sounded so natural despite using the technique.

Along with the techniques on breathing and speaking using a deep, costal breath, we were given practical exercises to do. For instance, we had to go into the street and put on 'voluntary stammering'. We had to stammer so badly that people would walk away. It was called the 'walk-away' routine. There was also the 'hang-up' routine, where you stammer so much on the phone that the person on the other end hangs up. Of course, the worst fear for a stammerer is for someone to walk away or hang up when you're trying to say something, so this confronts your fear. You just get used to it.

Also, they have a follow-up system where you have to phone and speak to McGuire coaches regularly and at any time. You tell them how you got on that day or that week and discuss any problems you may have had. I think it is this back-up service that enables the McGuire technique to be successful. You feel that you can talk to someone who knows about your problems at any time and not just at the appointed half-hour of your speech therapy sessions. Without that I don't think it would work.

I haven't got the fluency that I want yet, but I'm a lot better than I used to be. The trouble with me is that I don't just want 'better', I want it all: game, set and match. I feel it is my right. But getting over a chronic stammer does take time.

· *Jalal* ·

Jalal started stammering from about the age of four. Although he was very shy, the stammer did not give him any major problems during his childhood in Bangladesh. He is one of 10 children but the only one who stammers. However, two of his uncles are stammerers. Jalal's native tongue is Bengali and it was the only language spoken at home. He stammers to the same degree in both languages. Jalal came to England in 1988, at the age of 28, to study for his PhD in electrical engineering. Despite the fact that he is highly qualified, he has been unable to get a job appropriate to his academic achievements. He believes that this is due to his stammer.

I was very shy until I was 18. I didn't have any problems at home. My family were very helpful. Also school was OK. I didn't have any problems there. But I didn't like to go visiting. I don't know why, but I thought people would ask me things I would not be able to answer and this would give me problems.

I became a bit more free at 18. I didn't think about the stammering too much and it changed slowly. It got a little better.

In Bangladesh I had speech therapy for two months and it was helpful to start off with, but I didn't feel I was progressing enough to continue, so

I stopped. Some time later I went to see a hypnotist. I had to lie on a bed and he talked to me, suggesting to me that I didn't stammer. I went to him for about two months as well. I found it helped a lot for a time. In fact, after that I was better for quite a few years.

I came to England in 1988 and slowly, over a period of two years, my stammer deteriorated. I think it was probably the pressure of studying and maybe the change. It was a stressful period of time. But my stammer has not really improved to how it was before I left Bangladesh.

Before I left I had been talking to a man on the telephone for about half an hour. I felt that the conversation had gone very well. Anyway, in 1994 I went back to Bangladesh for a visit. I happened to speak to the same man again. He was amazed that I was stammering. He asked me how I had suddenly become a stammerer. I said I had always had this problem. He said he had never noticed it before.

Socially it is not too bad. I don't have too many problems talking to my wife or my boy. If I talk slowly, it's OK. If I start to talk fast, I have problems. I am better with people whom I know. When I meet people for the first time my stammer can be bad, but once I get to know them my attitude changes and my stammer gets better.

My main problem is with work. I have found that I have been passed by for better jobs time and time again. People who do not have as high qualifications and performance as I do get placed in more superior jobs. I'm sure it is because of my stammer.

In Bangladesh we don't have as many rules as there are here. It's funny, but despite all the helpful legislation in the UK, there is more discrimination here. I feel that this is compounded by underlying racial discrimination. In Bangladesh, after I had been working in an office for eight years I was able to do a teaching job for seven hours a week. I enjoyed it. I don't stammer anywhere near as much when I'm lecturing as when I am speaking normally. The classes were quite big. There were about 40 in each. I didn't have a problem and nor did the students. I taught for about 14 months.

I have tried to get a teaching job in the UK. I applied for six posts and got six interviews but I was never asked back. Each interview lasted for half an hour and I stammered in them more than at any other time because I was so nervous. I couldn't explain to them that I am not normally so bad and that when it comes to lecturing my stammer is so much better.

When employers see my qualifications and contributions they are impressed, but when they speak to me they are not so happy.

8

SPEECH THERAPY

Speech therapy has moved on a great deal in recent years. People who stammer are individuals, each with their own perceptions and needs and particular requirements for working on their speech. Furthermore, there is no hard evidence to indicate that stammering is a specifically neurological, psychological or any other type of problem. Many people believe that stammering is caused by a number of different factors and speech and language therapists are taking an increasingly flexible approach to stammering and offering their clients a programme tailor-made to their needs.

Rosemarie Hayhow is a speech and language therapist who is known for her eclectic approach. She explains:

> People who stammer are so different to each other. Although there are a lot of similarities in stammering and we can recognise and label the condition, the ways in which people are going to learn to live with it more comfortably are as individual as the people themselves. You have to listen to what they are saying in order to try and work out the best way to help them.
>
> Many years ago I became interested in Personal Construct Psychology and there are things from that which I still use. One of the basic beliefs is that there isn't an absolute reality. We all construe things in our own particular way and the way we construe things determines the way in which we behave. There is always a link between our understanding of things and our behaviour.
>
> It also works in reverse, in that the way we behave affects the way we think. Since everyone construes things in a slightly different way it cannot be assumed that one person's understanding of a problem is the same as another's.
>
> My starting point has to be to listen to the person who comes for help to try and understand their problem in their own terms. So if someone tells me that it is purely a speaking problem for them and they want to deal with it as such, I would accept that as a starting point. We would look very much at the behaviour

that was causing the problems and work on ways of modifying that.

It may happen that after a while the person may say that they believe that the way they have been thinking is also influencing their behaviour. I would allow them to come to this in their own time.

Someone else may come along and say that they know that it is not to do with behaviour, but they believe they stammer because of how they are thinking about people in relation to their stammering. If this is what they want to work on, I would use the Personal Construct model and work on their beliefs.

Personal Construct Psychology is explained in more detail further on in this chapter.

Some people who stammer say they tried speech therapy in the past and it did not work for them. Others for whom therapy was unsuccessful at first report that when they tried again several years later, they got much more out of it.

There can be many reasons for these experiences. First of all, some therapists work well with some clients and not with others and vice versa. Sometimes you gel and sometimes you don't. Another, perhaps more significant, factor to consider is that any kind of therapy is a two-way street. The client needs to work with the therapist to maximise the chances of achieving the desired result. Sadly, there are no guarantees or magic wands.

Sometimes people go for speech therapy hoping that the therapist will miraculously make their dysfluency vanish. This is understandable. If you are fed up with the way things are, frustrated by your communication problems and generally feeling helpless and hopeless, it takes considerable courage and motivation to knock at a therapist's door. For stammerers who find it difficult even to acknowledge that they stammer, the mere act of seeking therapy is a big step. Having done so, expecting the therapist to do the rest may not seem too much to ask. Unfortunately, it just doesn't work that way. You get out of therapy what you put into it and knocking on the door is only the first step.

Different treatments and techniques suit different people and the needs and requirements of each individual also change with time. What didn't suit you some years ago may suit you now. Not only has speech and language therapy changed over the years; you may have changed too.

'An analogy that I find useful is one of a bird trapped in a room, beating against the window and trying to get out,' says Rosemarie Hayhow. She goes on:

There may be an open window next to the closed one, but the bird is not going to see it. It is in such a panic that all it can do is to try and get out of that one window that is closed. Stammering is a bit like that. When a person is stammering they may believe that they have one way out of it and that is the way that they always try. It is their particular way of dealing with things. Like the bird, all they can see at that moment is that particular way out. When you are offering somebody a technique you are, in a way, showing them the open window. But if they are in a panic they can't use the open window, because they can't see it at that time.

People who make best use of me are the ones who come along really feeling they want to get on top of it. Enough is enough. They want to crack it. People like that are often very good at using therapy time in constructive ways. I am thinking of a few people I have worked with recently. Each time they come for therapy I always try to finish the session with a very definite task or something that they are going to do. This task evolves from the discussion we have had in the session. It might be on behaviour or the way they are thinking about something or it could be about the way they are preparing something. The task can be practical or it can be observational. People who do well come back the next session with lots to say about the tasks that have been set. They are really taking it seriously as a job to be done.

People with this kind of motivation normally come up with what the next thing is that they want to work on. My job is very much guiding them along. I think it is to do with a real determination to do something about their dysfluency and an acknowledgement of their responsibility in dealing with it. What is also significant is that they are prepared to work and are able to be open with me so that we can work on the right things.

One woman whom I have just started seeing was quite clear in our discussions at the initial interview that her breathing patterns were wrong. When she starts stammering she gets very tense and her breathing is very shallow. She feels that this leads to more tension and more stammering. She was convinced that this was a very important aspect of her stammering. So we went through breathing. We did some breathing exercises and made sure that she could tell the difference between shallow breathing and the deeper, diaphragmatic breathing. We worked out the kind of practice she should be doing to make that breathing pattern more accessible. We also discussed the times when she could be particularly monitoring her breathing and having a go at changing it. At the following session she was able to tell me about the practice she had done, whether or not she was able to change her breathing pattern while she was talking and, if so, in what situations she could do that. We then built on from that.

There is one client who always feels that his back is against the wall when he is talking. He has the feeling that people are making harsh judgements of him when he is talking. He is sure that he is going to stammer and lose control of his speech. He is actually a good communicator and has plenty of fluency, but when he stammers it is quite bad. After discussion, we decided that one of the first things for him to do was to look more at people. By looking down or away he was not allowing himself to see whether his fears were justified. So the first thing for him was to look at people more. He came back the next week and discussed who he had looked at more and with what effect. He could chart what he had done.

Another thing he needed to be able to do was to take more control of conversations. We realised that he very rarely asked questions, but always waited for people to ask him. So he was always in that defensive position of waiting to see what he was going to be asked. We did some work first of all on the questions that people might ask. This is just the kind of work you might do with people who are doing a course on communication skills. We talked about why it is difficult to ask questions and, of course, we talked about the emotional side of it as well. We explored what the implications were for him in asking questions. It can be very threatening when you begin to take more control.

We discussed all these things but at the end of the session we needed something concrete to work on. We talked quite care-fully about what would be a good situation to try and ask more questions as well as the sorts of questions that would be safe ones to ask.

Whatever the content of the session may be, and sometimes it is much more to do with feelings and fears, I make sure that the task is a concrete one. But there are lots of times when the task is very difficult because of the feelings of fear involved.

So working on the fear component of stammering has to be a major part of practising any therapeutic technique. The David McGuire intensive courses that Nav talks about in Chapter Seven is an example of tackling this fear component in a direct and confrontational way. 'We had to go into the street and put on "voluntary stammering",' he explains. 'We had to stammer so badly that people would walk away. . . . There was also the hang-up routine, where you stammer so much on the phone that the person on the other end hangs up.' This kind of approach works well for some people, but not for others. It is a case of horses for courses.

Many speech and language therapists can offer group therapy and individual therapy depending on what the client requires. If the work that is to be done is on a very personal level and needs to focus on the client's own emotions and way of thinking, individual therapy, which provides a chance to talk about things one to one and on a confidential basis, is likely to be the most appropriate.

However, group therapy can be extremely effective in treating stammering, for several reasons. People benefit from group therapy because it gives them an opportunity to meet others with similar problems to talk and exchange ideas and learn from each other's experiences. They can practise techniques on one another without fear of being misunderstood or ridiculed. Therapists sometimes form groups where the participants share a particular difficulty, as Rosemarie Hayhow explains:

> At the moment I've got a group of students who all stammer quite mildly but who have anxiety about presentation work. This work is best done in a group. The members of another group are currently working on extending their use of those strategies that they find helpful. They are usually able to handle their stammering well but need help in dealing with stressful situations. They learn from each others' experiences as well as gaining support from the group.

There is not always the opportunity to shop around for suitable speech and language therapists. Their availability varies in different parts of the country. Some work within the NHS and others work privately. Assuming you have a choice, what should you look for?

A speech and language therapist who has had some additional training in stammering can be a good starting point, but it is not an absolute necessity. Someone who feels that their problem is as much to do with what is going on below the visible level of the iceberg as above it may be better off looking for a therapist who has had some additional training in counselling. Someone who is keen to work on the practical skills of fluency may need to find a therapist who focuses on this aspect of stammering. If they want to deal with the emotions surrounding their stammer as well, they can work on this with a counsellor or psychotherapist.

When you do find a therapist, if possible, think of the first session very much as an exploration, followed by negotiation. You first explore the parameters of the problem and the ways in which it can be helped. Then you discuss what you feel you can or cannot do as part of the therapy. One approach may be right to begin with, and another later on. Someone who stammers might start with some intensive work on fluency control. Once they have reached a higher level of fluency, they can work on other things.

Some people who stammer say that they can master the techniques and use them well in the clinic with the speech and language therapist, but when they get outside, the techniques fail them. One reason for this may be that many people do not realise the importance of practising in the real world.

Speech therapy techniques are rarely one-dimensional. They are just one component. Other factors are needed to make them work, such as a basic acceptance that you stammer, and the ability to deal with the fears that accompany your stammering. Some people find it easier to tackle these fears head on, while others need to take it much more gently. The only right way is the one that works for you.

· *Personal Construct Psychology (PCP)* ·

This counselling approach focuses on the whole person and therefore includes the emotional, social and psychological aspects of stammering rather than being concerned only with correcting the speech itself. It has more to do with what is below the surface of the stammering iceberg than what is above it. Many speech and language therapists use it in tandem with the more physical techniques like slow prolonged speech and block modification.

PCP entails understanding what stammering means to each person individually. Explaining the concept in her book *Counselling People with Communication Problems*, published by Sage Publications, Peggy Dalton, who is Consultant Clinician at the Centre for Personal Construct Psychology in London, says:

Most counselling approaches emphasize the importance of under-standing the clients' views of themselves and their problems, but PCP goes furthest, perhaps, in its exploration of how people experience their worlds, how they make sense of themselves and others and the very personal meaning to them of the difficulties they present. Although counsellors have their professional understanding of the anxieties and obstacles which beset those who seek their help, it is the clients' perceptions of the source of those anxieties or the enormity of the obstacles with which we have to work. Our first priority, therefore, is to help them to clarify what is troubling them in the context of their experience of life as a whole.'

The theory is that the way we are and the way we behave are based on how we have learnt to anticipate the things that happen to us. The PCP practitioner will listen to what the client is saying and work out what it means within the context of his or her inner world, working on the premise that it is only the client's individual perception that is of importance. This may be very different to that of the counsellor or any-one else.

The therapist will elicit from the client a series of 'constructs' by a process of comparison and contrasts. According to PCP, we often con-strue things in terms of opposites, so that a person is warm or cold, and an event fun or tedious, for example. If you have generally experi-enced going to the cinema as fun, you will anticipate it as such. If you have found sitting exams or going to the dentist unpleasant in the past, you will expect it to be so in the future.

For a stammerer, tasks like ordering a meal in a restaurant, answer-ing the telephone or buying a train ticket may have been uncomfort-able experiences, so he or she will continue to anticipate them with dread. The chances are that he will avoid them whenever possible. The aim of Personal Construct Psychology is to shift the association between discomfort or embarrassment and feared events, such as ordering a meal in a restaurant. If the client is eventually able to go out and choose what he wants to eat from a menu and order it without feelings of trepidation, he will have altered his personal construction of that particular situation.

Constructs are not just thoughts, they exist in all our senses includ-ing sight, hearing and touch. We may perceive a sound to be loud or soft; an object may look beautiful or ugly, and feel smooth or rough. How we construe things, whether in verbalised thoughts or with our senses, is very personal to each of us. Peggy Dalton explains:

All these constructs, whether easily verbalised or experienced as feelings, abstract or more concrete, core or peripheral are linked together to form a 'construct system'. And it is through this system that a person develops theories about things in order to know how to approach the world. Experience of events and people will modify these theories and elaborate them as we grow older. Our sense of ourselves will change as we become involved in more aspects of life. Learning something new will initiate new ideas. New relationships will evoke new feelings. Validation or invalidation from others will contribute to the overall picture of ourselves at any point in time.

Bit by bit the therapist will build up a picture of the client within the framework of his or her personal constructs. Some attention will probably be paid to past (including childhood) experiences, but the main focus will be on the here and now: who the client is, how he feels about himself, his difficulties, the people he lives with or meets and what he wants or expects from life.

Armed with an insight into the client's individual world, the therapist will aim to help him alter some of the constructs that may be holding him back and preventing him from achieving what he wants from life.

Adult clients who stammer are often asked to write a character sketch of themselves in the early stages of their therapy. This introduces the therapist into the world of the client. Much of the work is done through talking, but often the therapist will suggest forms of behaviour modification, admitting to being a stammerer, for instance. One client may never have ordered a meal in a restaurant because he is ashamed of his stammer and he doesn't want anyone to know about it. If, during the course of therapy he can go into a restaurant and say to the waitress: 'I stammer so you'll have to bear with me,' he may well find that the waitress is not at all forbidding and is prepared to wait quite patiently for his request. If he does this a few times he may be able to alter two personal constructs: first, that he must hide his stammer and, second, that he cannot order a meal in a restaurant. Needless to say, this may take some time and effort to achieve.

Sometimes clients move forward when they change their constructs about other people. They may view others in a very polarised way. For instance, a client may regard a woman he knows, who doesn't seem shy, as an extrovert. This may be the case. She may be hiding her insecurity in a show of confidence. Or she may be confident in some situations and timid in others. If he can stand back and view her outside his polarised construct, he may get a very different picture of her. And, as his perception of his friend is adjusted, so is his view of himself. He no longer sees the woman as an extrovert or himself as wholly shy.

Similarly, a client may think his boss is very demanding and holds all the power in the relationship. But if he can value himself more highly and realise that his boss is actually quite dependent on his skills and knowledge, the relationship will proceed on a different footing. Altering the construct will change the way he approaches the situation.

Some stammerers construe the condition itself in a polarised way, contrasting stammering with being fluent. However, many non-stammerers actually speak in an extremely incoherent way. Stammerers often perceive their stammering as much more intrusive than it is, believing themselves to be much more difficult to listen to than they really are.

One stammerer I interviewed for this book told me that he and his colleagues at work had attended a series of lectures where one of the lecturers stammered. He said that he could not understand what the man was saying because of his stammer, *but none of his colleagues had a problem with it*. None of them complained that they couldn't understand and since he was an experienced lecturer the chances were that he was understood perfectly well by everyone else. My interviewee's construct of stammering was such that he perceived anyone who stammered as difficult to understand. This was probably not the case with the lecturer and it certainly was not so with the interviewee himself.

A practitioner of Personal Construct Psychology will often produce a grid of their clients' personal constructs which will include the contrasting perceptions that influence their lives. For instance, the grid may include 'socially confident' and 'insecure', 'assertive' and 'diffident', 'articulate' and 'dysfluent'. Early on in therapy, the client will rate his score according to where he feels he is in relation to being assertive or not, confident or not and so on. Later he will rate himself again and at the end of therapy he can assess how far he has or has not progressed.

· *Assertiveness Training* ·

Some speech and language therapists run courses on assertiveness training for stammerers. These take place in a group setting and usually include between eight and ten people who stammer.

The aim is to help people to feel and behave more assertively. This means feeling more able to say what they want; being able to say no in certain situations; learning to handle criticism effectively, and being able to give criticism; and learning to express feelings more easily.

During the course, they will learn specific skills. There will be work on non-verbal communication to enable them to look and sound more assertive. Body language is important. The way you stand, gesture and respond gives people messages about you. Maintaining relaxed eye contact is assertive. Amongst other things, it tells people that you are in control of yourself, you know what you're talking about and you mean what you say. They will also be taught verbal skills like sticking to the point and not being diverted, to help them to relate verbally in a more assertive way. A great deal of role-play is involved.

Videos are usually used in these courses to give people feedback on both the non-verbal and verbal aspects of their behaviour. In this way they become much more aware of how they are communicating.

The theory is that there are four basic patterns of behaviour. There is *direct aggression*, where people are bossy, arrogant, intolerant, opinionated, overbearing and bulldozing. Or you can be *indirectly aggressive*, in which case you may be sarcastic, deceiving, manipulating, ambiguous, insinuating or guilt-inducing. *Passive* behaviour is when the person is helpless, moaning, submissive, indecisive and apologetic. If you are *assertive*, you are direct, honest, positive, accepting, responsible and spontaneous.

So how would you behave assertively in a real-life situation? Imagine, for instance, that you've lent some money to a friend and he hasn't given it back. How can you handle that? You can let it go, which would be *passive*. Or you might be a bit sarcastic, and try to find a way of getting back the money without asking for it. This would be *indirect aggression*. On the other hand, you could be *aggressive* and shout at your friend, telling him that you'll never lend him money again because he cannot be trusted to give it back. (This is an unusual scenario, but it can happen.) Finally, you could be *assertive*. This entails being open about how you feel.

If you're feeling apprehensive about bringing the up subject, you might start off by saying: 'I do feel a bit uncomfortable mentioning this, but I lent you £50 a month ago and I would be really grateful if I could have it back.' When you handle a situation assertively, you say what you feel and you say what you want.

If you were doing this in a role-play situation on a course, there would be two of you and you would take it in turns to be the lender and the borrower. At the end of each enactment you would tell the other person how it felt. This gives you practice at being more direct.

Sometimes role-plays involve three people so that one person observes the dialogue and gives feedback. If you start to behave more assertively, you should begin to feel more confident and this may have a direct or indirect effect on your level of fluency.

Carolyn Cheasman, a speech and language therapist who runs assertiveness training courses at the City Literary Institute (City Lit) in London, comments:

> If someone is unsure or indecisive about confronting somebody, that feeling of uncertainty or indecision is likely to lead them to feel unsure about themselves in that particular situation. On the assertiveness course one of the big aspects that we look at is what we call *rights*. If you start to get in touch with these and feel that you do have a *right*, for example to say what you feel, take things back to a shop and so on, you will begin to feel better about yourself and more confident.

During these courses, group members also learn skills to enable them to handle confrontational situations more effectively. This helps to increase their confidence and for some people this will have a knock-on effect on their level of fluency.

The assertiveness course at the City Lit is more suitable for people who have already had some speech therapy. This is because the idea is to put the stammering on one side and deal with the behaviour that surrounds it. As Carolyn Cheasman says:

> Being more assertive can help your speech, just as knowing some speech skills for your stammer will help you feel more confident and to be more assertive. A lot of people who stammer have a network of avoidance behaviour that can manifest itself in speech in the form of 'umming' and 'ahhing' and trying to swap words around, all of which is very unassertive. In speech therapy they are helped to be more open and direct about their stammer and therefore if they have had some speech therapy they should already be more open and upfront.

The fear of stammering will interfere with people's ability to be assertive. Someone may, for instance, be worried about saying 'no' to a neighbour when asked to baby-sit for fear that the neighbour might not like them any more. If the person is a stammerer who is still nervous about his speech, he or she will be worried about how to say 'no' without losing the goodwill of the neighbour and, in addition to that, he or she may be afraid of stammering.

'On the course we try to focus on the fact that it might not be just the stammer that makes the person unassertive. We try to broaden it out really,' adds Cheasman. 'So you are putting the stammering to one side and looking at the person's feelings more broadly.'

You can respond to the request for baby-sitting in four different ways:

- You could be *aggressive* and say something like: 'I'm sorry, but I've got better things to do with my time.'
- You could be *passive* and cancel any previous engagement you had or put to one side the fact that the last thing in the world you want to do is to baby-sit and do it anyway.
- You could handle the situation in an *indirectly aggressive* and guilt-producing way by saying something like: 'I don't know very much about children. I'm sure you wouldn't dream of leaving your children in the hands of someone as inexperienced as I am, would you?'
- The *assertive* way of reacting, if you did not want to baby-sit, would be to say that you could not do it and, perhaps, give a reason.

Carolyn Cheasman says:

The important thing is to be direct and come to the point and not to try and drown it in a whole mass of excuses and justification. You have to believe in the right to say 'no'. I personally think it is quite important sometimes to say why. Some assertiveness trainers say that it is all right to say 'no' and not to give a reason but I, personally, don't always feel comfortable with that.

People can say why, but not in a cringing, apologetic way. They can, at times, be confronting quite difficult things in their relationships.

As stammerers become more fluent and more outgoing, they sometimes find themselves in more frequent confrontational situations. If they have avoided stammering they may, deliberately or unconsciously, have avoided quite difficult situations. They may have avoided becoming involved in meetings at work, or they may have avoided conflicts within those meetings. As they become more open about stammering and feel more ready to take part in arguments or confrontations, they may need to learn how to handle these situations. This is where assertiveness training can be very helpful.

As Carolyn Cheasman explains:

People have to identify their fears as well as the situations that scare them. They have to think about setting themselves targets and work on things hierarchically. This means going into a situation in which you have a slight fear and saying what you want without hiding the stammer. You then build up to behaving in this way in more and more difficult situations.

It is a long-term process and quite a difficult and challenging one. But that is what it is, essentially facing the fear and going ahead and saying what you want to say in an assertive way.

Some stammerers want to be more assertive about using speech therapy techniques. They want to confront the stammering itself. One of the rights a person can give themselves is the right to stammer. That is something which people can very much relate to. In speech therapy we do a lot on what we call *desensitisation*, which is working on becoming less sensitive and more open to stammering. There are very direct links between desensitisation and assertiveness. It is to do with openness, honesty and acceptance and being more in touch with what you are feeling.

The address of City Lit appears in the Useful Addresses section at the end of the book.

· *Steve* ·

My first recollection is when I was at infant school. I think I was about seven years old. The headmistress thought there was a problem because of my speech. I was taken to a doctor in a local government surgery who stripped me naked and gave me a physical examination. He thought I was stammering because I was an abused child and he was looking for bruising.

My parents were present and they went crazy. It is still spoken about now.

When it was obvious that I wasn't being abused they put me in touch with the speech therapy department at the local clinic. I saw the speech therapist there until I was 15 years old without much success.

I remember being taught syllabic speaking. I had to talk to a metronome. I had to talk to a mirror. My parents bought me a spool tape recorder and I used to speak into that and do reading exercises.

I tried to do this syllabic speech at school. It was the time when Dr. Who was just starting to get popular on TV. Do you remember the famous daleks? I was a dalek then.

I had the mickey taken out of me. It wasn't very funny. I tended to turn the other cheek but sometimes it really did get to the core. So I didn't use this syllabic speech with my friends. I just went on merrily stammering. It was easier.

You put up your own walls. Stammering didn't bother me. I didn't lose any sleep over it. But I would have chosen not to stammer.

I stopped going to speech therapy in my last year of school. I stayed on to do my CSEs because there weren't any job openings. I loved woodwork but there were no apprenticeships for joiners. They were starting to mass-produce everything. In the end I managed to get an apprenticeship in an engineering firm and I've been there ever since. That's nearly 30 years ago. I'm more or less programmed to clock in and out of the factory.

In the early 1980s I had a skin problem and I went to see a dermatologist at a local hospital. When I went into his office I couldn't say my name or answer any of his questions. He asked: 'What on earth is the matter with you? How long have you been like this?' He told me that before he examined me he was going to make me an appointment to see a speech therapist.

You'll never believe that he got me an appointment with the same speech therapist I'd been seeing from the ages of seven to 15. She was quite long in the tooth by now!

Eventually I was referred to a young man at our local teaching hospital who put me on the right step. He didn't so much treat the stammer as treat me. He made me think about my problem in a different way. I enjoyed going there which is half the problem solved.

After about six months he asked me if I would like to attend an intensive course that the hospital was running. It was like opening a new door. It was fantastic. We practised various techniques like block modification and slow prolonged speech, where we had to really slow down. We did role-plays, video feedback and worked on desensitisation.

It was the first time I was fluent. At the end of the fortnight I had no twitches, grimaces, slavering or spitting. But what was more important, I met other stammerers, some of whom had a worse problem than I had. Until then I had thought that it was only me who had these difficulties.

Before that course I would never use a telephone. If I'd got to use one I'd get my friends at work to phone up for me. If there was a phone ringing I would never answer it. One of the things we did on the course was learn to use the telephone. We were taught telephone techniques. I don't give it a second thought now. Occasionally you will get someone on the other end who has never spoken to a stammerer and they will ridicule you. It happens, but I don't let it bother me.

If I really put my mind to it I have no need to stammer. But sometimes I forget and lapse into old habits. What has worked for me is learning to control my speech. Learning to breathe and speak very much more slowly and also not avoiding but trying to use better words. I stammer much more if I use slang. If I don't, I find I can control my speaking better.

If I speak with friends I get excited and I jabber on and I stammer. If I can slow down and stand back I can gain control. My wife is always telling me to slow down when I stammer. She says I don't need to stammer. It can be infuriating but she's perfectly right.

I go to a local self-help group for stammerers. It's the young stammerers I really feel for. Some of the youngsters who are in their teens are very introverted. I sometimes wonder if I was like that then. I'm now in my mid-forties.

Stammering has never really stopped me doing anything. I was always part of a crowd but I was always on the edge of it. I was never the key player. I maybe didn't push myself forward enough.

Over the last ten years I've become quite outspoken at work. I'll speak to anybody, including the managing director. I've no problems about it. If I get into difficulties I'll usually explain that I've got a speech impediment and I'm OK with it. It's amazing how much easier that makes the other parties feel. It really works. I wish I'd known that trick years ago.

My friends and I have quite a laugh about my stammer. I don't think a lot of stammerers can laugh about their problem. But it has helped me, being able to laugh. In the old days when I laughed about it, it was forced laughter. Now I have to have a chuckle about it myself. I suppose I can see the funny side now because of the desensitisation and also because I feel so much more confident in myself.

I've got two children aged five and six and a half. I used to be paranoid that they would grow up with a stammer. But I've got two beautiful girls who could talk a glass eye to sleep. I've nothing to fear.

9

PERSONAL GROWTH

This chapter looks at some of the 'talking treatments' available. None of them deals with speech itself, but with the emotions that surround stammering, with what is going on below the sea-level of the iceberg.

These kinds of talking treatment help people dispose of unwanted and destructive emotional luggage. They are also very useful in current emotional situations. If you are going through a bad patch or an unhappy period of your life, talking to a therapist can help you express your anger and hurt, and in so doing, ease the pain.

The point to remember is that these treatments are not supposed to be a destructive process – quite the contrary. The aim of peeling back the layers and discovering more about yourself is to strengthen you, give you more personal power and enable you to feel good about yourself.

Many other talking treatments are available in addition to these outlined here.

· *Rational Emotive Behaviour Therapy* · *(REBT)*

This is one of the best-known cognitive behavioural therapies and it follows a much more direct approach than psychotherapy or counselling, which are also outlined in this chapter. Prof. Windy Dryden, one of the foremost figures in counselling and cognitive behaviour therapy in the United Kingdom, is the leading exponent of REBT in this country. He has written and edited over 100 books. Prof. Dryden is also a person who stammers. These days, he stammers very occasionally, but as a child and as an adolescent he stammered quite severely. Many of the strategies that Dryden used to overcome the problems of stammering are those employed by practitioners of Rational Emotive Behaviour Therapy.

REBT therapists help clients to identify, challenge and change their irrational beliefs. They strive to accept their clients unconditionally and with empathy while helping them to dispel their irrational ideas.

Although it is a much more directive and challenging relationship than in some other disciplines, therapists are expected to be supportive of their clients and respond to them as fallible and often hurting human beings, without building an over-dependent relationship.

One of the motivating factors for Prof. Dryden was hearing Michael Bentine saying in a radio broadcast that he had got over his anxiety about stammering by not worrying about it. If he stammered, he stammered; too bad. 'I took that attitude and developed it,' says Prof. Dryden. 'I saw that I had been avoiding speaking and I had also been using various tricks that people who stammer tend to do. I decided that I wouldn't avoid and I wouldn't use any tricks any more.'

One of the first things he did as an older teenager was to change his name:

> For a person who stammers, David Denbin is hardly the world's greatest name to have. I used to say, 'My name is Enbin but it begins with a D.' But people found that even more strange than stammering. I had difficulty with consonants that preceded vowels.
>
> I had had speech therapy as a child and one of the suggestions had been that I should learn the saxophone. I played it poorly. When I was working on a kibbutz in my teens I was nicknamed 'Windy', so I decided to change my first name to that and Dryden was the telephone exchange in the area in which I lived. I had no difficulty with saying Dryden because it was a D followed by another consonant. It was much softer than Denbin.

In the REBT tradition of challenging absolutes, musts, oughts and shoulds and pursuing the 'wants', Prof. Dryden legally changed his name to one he could say without stammering. 'It was my name,' he says. 'I could do what I wanted with it.'

As a child, Prof. Dryden experienced teasing in both primary and secondary schools. He believes that this experience may have been one of the reasons that he pursued a career in counselling and cognitive behaviour therapy, following his psychology degree and a PhD in Self-Disclosure. He says:

> I guess I am the archetypal wounded healer. I felt hurt and angry at the time about being teased for having a stammer. I became aware of my own emotions and also interested in human behaviour and the way people act. Some people would be very nice to me when they were on their own and then, as soon as half an hour later, when they were in a group, they could start teasing

me. I was intrigued by this so I became interested in psychology and eventually in counselling.

It took me time to get over the anxiety of stammering. But I decided that no matter which situation I was in, even if all I said was a couple of words, I would say something. In my early twenties I would go to debating societies and places like that and I would resolve to always speak, whether I stammered or not. One of the things I discovered quite clearly was that I was really overestimating the amount of negative reaction I would get. You're always going to get some, but you don't get as much as you think you're going to have. So now, even when I am going through a bad patch, I still speak up. I won't stop speaking. If I am stammering, I allow myself to stammer.

In addition to his tremendous output in writing, Prof. Dryden is a university lecturer, teaching psychology and counselling. He is also involved in REBT training and therapy.

In treating a person who stammers, an REBT therapist will consider the emotional conflicts that surround the stammering. He or she will work on the client's anxiety about the prospect of stammering. Clients may be ashamed about stammering and they may also be unduly worried about other people's reactions. The therapist will look at those emotional problems and help the client to identify, challenge and change the irrational beliefs which underpin those emotions. Prof. Dryden comments:

I am not sure that I would get people to deliberately stammer. But I would certainly get them to speak and to look quite carefully at stopping any camouflaging methods that they were using or avoidance techniques and things like that. I would work out a programme where we would agree a hierarchy of things that need working on. It would be at a challenging rate but not an overwhelming one. I wouldn't hire the Albert Hall and ask my clients to speak to a large audience but if, for instance, they had a problem with speaking on the telephone, we would work directly on that.

Dealing assertively with people who finish sentences for those who stammer is something else REBT clients can learn to handle. 'You get some people who think they are doing you a favour by trying to talk for you,' explains Prof. Dryden. 'People who stammer help themselves a great deal by learning to tell them politely but firmly that they prefer to speak for themselves.'

However, the underlying goal is to shift the perception of stammering itself. In his late teens Prof. Dryden realised that he had been defining himself as a stammerer and he decided to redefine himself as a person who stammered at times, spoke fluently at other times and did a thousand and one other things as well. He believes that it is very important for people who stammer to make this change in their attitude towards themselves in order to progress.

If they are fairly healthy individuals in other areas of their lives, I think about 10 to 15 sessions is all they would need. I would space those sessions out so that there was plenty of time to practise in between. I wouldn't be working on speech techniques because that it is not my area of expertise.

I see myself as a psychological educator teaching a method and I would detail the treatment approach. If the client was agreeable to it we would embark upon the treatment. This would focus on getting them over their anxiety and, if it existed, their feelings of shame. I would encourage them to speak as fluently as they could but not to stop communicating because they were afraid to stammer. If you do that you just re-confirm old attitudes. If you decide to keep quiet you are really saying that you are not prepared to speak in case you stammer because it is so terrible to stammer. I encourage people to accept that if they are going to avoid anything it should be their avoidances.

A great deal of the therapy is rooted in everyday life because that is where people need to make the changes.

There are REBT therapists in different areas of the country and the address of the national organisation appears in Useful Addresses at the end of the book.

· *Psychotherapy* ·

Psychotherapists believe that the sort of person you are is based to a large extent on your childhood. This can be a mixture of many things: how you were brought up; what expectations your parents had of you, and how they behaved towards you; your place in the family pecking order; the behaviour patterns you unconsciously learnt from your parents and brothers and sisters; your experiences with friends and at school, and so on. Together with the genetic characteristics you were born with, all these factors have combined to make up the individual you now are. If you stammer, issues of communication throughout your life will almost certainly have made a significant contribution to your current psychological make-up.

It is a psychotherapist's job to help you unlock some of your emotional doors and find the clues that will help you to understand why you behave the way you do, both in terms of stammering and other aspects of your life. Looking at these issues in a deep and sympathetic way can often release the block, so to speak, and give you the confidence in yourself to join in and take a full part in life in spite of your speech problems.

Psychotherapy examines the external and internal worlds. Our external world is what takes place in daily life and how we react to people and events. Our internal world consists of our conscious and unconscious thoughts, fantasies, dreams and memories. Psychotherapy aims to make some of our unconscious dreams, fears and desires conscious. Getting to know and understand the internal world is the art of psychotherapy.

Stammering may indicate a conflict in communication. The stammerer wants to communicate, but cannot do so as well as he needs. A psychotherapist will not be looking at the external or physical reasons for the problem, he or she will aim to find out the underlying cause. Stammering is seen as a symptom of internal conflict. As Judy Cooper, a psychotherapist, explains:

People have difficulty in expressing themselves either because of an internal conflict or because of their environment or because their family hasn't really been willing to hear what they have got to say. There are underlying reasons why speech has become a difficult means of expression and this is what has to be got at with the therapy.

In psychotherapy the person would be encouraged to say whatever came to mind concerning thoughts, dreams and memories. We would try to unravel the problems and understand where the trauma is coming from and try to help make it more conscious.

· *Matthew* ·

Matthew is a stammerer who went for psychotherapy. He was the eldest of four children and was in his mid-forties when he went for therapy. He had had some speech therapy but still stammered quite severely at times.

His parents were very critical, demanding and constantly at logger-

heads. His mother was a very volatile woman with a sharp tongue. Neither parent showed their offspring very much tactile affection or warmth.

Most of the rows between the parents took place at night when Matthew was in bed but not asleep. The ferocity of the rows, which occasionally ended in violence, would frighten him and he would lie under the covers trying not to listen. Sometimes Matthew was an onlooker at his parents' fights. In therapy he recalled one occasion when the shouting was particularly loud and he heard his parents throwing the crockery at each other. He heard his mother screaming as his father hit her. The next morning his father left home and did not return for nearly a year.

Matthew recalled that incident several times in therapy and each time he got in touch more and more with the fear he had experienced as a small child. Bringing the fear into the conscious in the presence of the protective therapist, helped Matthew to dispel it. He was now experiencing the fear as an adult and not as a small, helpless child who was totally reliant on these two people who seemed to be doing terrible things to each other with words.

During the therapy Matthew had several dreams which helped bring into the open his deep-seated fears of inadequacy, some of which stemmed from being a paralysed bystander in his parents' rows. He couldn't protect his mother from his father's violence and he could not protect his father from his mother's whiplash tongue. He could not stop his father from leaving home. He wanted to speak out but he couldn't. He was too frightened. All he could do, whenever possible, was to hide.

Dream analysis

In order to unlock the doors to the patient's internal world the psychotherapist uses certain techniques. One of these is dream analysis. When a person is asleep and dreaming, he or she is open to moods and feelings that are blocked or overshadowed while awake. By analysing a person's dreams, the therapist can unveil and clarify feelings and emotions that are normally hidden from the patient.

Dream language is different to the language we use when we are conscious. When we are awake we communicate in words, but when we are asleep we communicate in visual images, and these often have a symbolic meaning. The therapist's skill lies in interpreting these symbols and understanding what they represent to the patient.

Freud believed that dreams express the unconscious desires the dreamer would not accept in waking life. In order to avoid facing up to his or her unconscious wishes, the dreamer censors the dream by disguising its true nature and underlying message. So there are two sides to the dream: the real meaning and the disguised or distorted form. To analyse the dream, the psychotherapist has to cut through the distortions and discover the true meaning.

Dreams have meanings on different levels and a number of different, equally correct, interpretations are possible. However, it is essential that the dream interpretation makes sense to the patient as well as the therapist.

Free association

This is another technique used by some psychotherapists. In free association, the patient says everything that comes into his or her head during the session, no matter how seemingly meaningless, embarrassing or unpleasant it may be. The client does not organise or make sense of these ideas, but allows them to flow spontaneously. This spontaneity should eventually uncover important memories or feelings that have been blocked off.

In Matthew's case, free association helped to bring back with intensity the feeling he had when, as a result of a row, his father left home. It helped him to get in touch with the fear and abandonment he had felt when his father left. In a way, he also got in touch with his fear of speaking. Had his parents not spoken and, more importantly, not shouted, his father would not have left. If his mother had not said things to his father that he did not want to hear, he would not have hit her. To some degree, speaking became associated in his mind with danger, violence and being abandoned.

Matthew was already a stammerer when this incident occurred, so it didn't trigger the stammering, but it may have been one of the things that helped to keep it in place.

Transference

Transference is another tool of the psychotherapist's trade. The patient transfers to the therapist the feelings and reactions he has related to other significant people in his life. From time to time, the therapist becomes the patient's mother, father, sibling or even employer. The feelings of anger, love, bitterness or fear that the patient has for his mother, father or whoever are projected on to the therapist.

Matthew's therapist became his mother and his father at different times in the therapy. But this time he had a 'mother' and 'father' he could talk to, who wouldn't shout, criticise or demand. On the contrary, Matthew was able to express his anger to the therapist without any fear of retaliation or repercussion. The parenting the therapist gave him was one that valued him without judging and, best of all, it allowed him to speak. During therapy Matthew's fluency fluctuated, but eventually his stammer was no longer the impediment it had once been in his life.

Judy Cooper comments:

When fear and anger are no longer repressed, people who have difficulty in communicating can speak more freely. It is really to do with where the energy lies. If the energy has been used to keep things blocked and repressed there is not so much energy for other things. If it is released, then the person is not so afraid of communication.

· *Counselling* ·

A counsellor's job is to look at the here and now and examine current patterns of behaviour. He or she will encourage you to talk freely, without fear of being judged or criticised in any way. But the counsellor is also trained to discover whether current feelings and behaviour are related to things that have happened in the past. He or she will delve a little into childhood and family background to try to get a clearer picture of you as a person. The counsellor will occasionally reflect back what you have said in order to untangle the web of feelings and emotions that comprise a particular situation. Over a period of time, this kind of examination of why you do the things you do can help you see yourself in a new light and understand more about your feelings and motivations.

Counselling can also help rid you of some of your emotional 'ghosts'. For instance, a negative self-image that may have been formed in childhood can be modified by talking about it, and unacknowledged anger can be expressed in a safe, caring environment.

Counselling can help you look at your relationships in a more constructive way, too. These may include your friendships, how you relate to people at work, and relationships with your wife, husband or partner. Talking to a therapist in an unguarded way often unlocks doors and makes clients feel more relaxed about relating to other people. Some people who stammer have said that their dysfluency sometimes created difficulties in their marriage.

Relate counsellors are trained particularly to deal with couples. The ꞌh Association for Counselling specialises more in one-to-one ꞌing. The national bodies of both are listed in Useful Addresses.

They can put you in touch with the centre or individual therapists in your area.

· *Person-centered Psychotherapy* ·

This therapy was founded by an American psychologist, Dr. Carl Rogers. Person-centred therapists believe that, given the right conditions, everyone can achieve a good feeling about themselves and realise their potential for self-fulfilment and happiness.

One of the necessary conditions is what therapists call 'unconditional positive regard' from therapist to client. This basically means that clients receive from the therapist a feeling that they are an OK person regardless of who they are, what they look like, how they speak and what they have done. There are no judgements.

Empathy is also considered to be essential if the client is to be able to change his or her self-perspective. This means that the therapist should understand who the client is, what he is feeling, what is his experience and its meaning and what he is trying to convey. The therapist is also required to be open and in touch with his or her own feelings and responses.

The idea behind the person-centred approach is that once people become more in touch with who they are and understand what they really want, they can start to develop in their own way. When they know what they want, as opposed to what other people want of them, they can begin to realise some of their own dreams and desires.

The therapist has no special interest in the client behaving in any particular way or being any particular kind of person. Therefore, the client can explore his or her own emotions and desires without any pressure or direction to be something or someone that family or friends may find acceptable. He is accepted for who he is at the time. This freedom of self-expression in an atmosphere of acceptance and confidentiality is believed to allow the patient to get to know himself and become the person he wants to be.

· *Helen* ·

Few situations can be more frightening than growing up in a house-hold where the people who are supposed to be looking after you and protecting you are physically and emotionally abusing you. This was Helen's experience.

Her alcoholic father used to hit her, particularly when he felt that she had said or done something wrong. Not only did her mother not intervene, but when, as a child, Helen was referred to a psychologist, her mother went with her and continually denied that anything untoward was happening at home. Here is Helen's story:

I started to be aware of stammering when I was about nine years old. I was always very quiet. I think I was afraid to speak. I was told off about stammering at home. They thought I was doing it to get attention. I felt I had to keep quiet to survive.

I was OK at school. I didn't mix very well, but I had a couple of friends. I was very quiet at school as well as at home so I don't think that even the teachers noticed it.

About a year or so after I'd started stammering I had a school medical. My stammer was picked up. They sent me to see a speech therapist, who reckoned it was psychological. She said I didn't stammer much when I was with her but there were certain words I couldn't say. I had problems with my B's and S's. She realised that I had a stammer, but she didn't think it was that bad.

She referred me to a psychologist. It was acknowledged there that I had a psychological problem, but my parents denied that anything could be wrong with me.

At the time my home life was all I knew, but I think that I suspected, even then, that things were not right. Now I realise what a crazy family I've come from.

I was abused emotionally and physically. My father was such a bully. He was an alcoholic. He abused my mother as well. He was very violent and I would see her being hit. I always remember being afraid of him, but he definitely got worse as the years went on. He used to slap me very hard. When his drinking really got out of control he became very violent. I was about twelve years old at the time.

I couldn't do sums at school and he used to make me learn my times tables and recite them to him. When I got them wrong, he used to slap me hard. I think that is when the stammering started.

Then he started hitting me for stammering. My mother didn't or couldn't do anything. She just let it carry on. I can see now that she couldn't protect herself from him, either. He was a bully and she was a doormat.

I went to see the psychologist about every six weeks to see how I was getting on. I had some kind of tests to see what my ability was. I think it surprised me when my parents were told that I was above average in everything but maths.

My parents were the sort of people who would deny that there could be anything wrong at home. As far as they were concerned, we were a normal family. We were a very small family, in fact, as we didn't have any extended family at all in the area. There were just the five of us. My two younger siblings don't stammer, but they didn't experience the abuse that I did. As the eldest, I definitely got the worst of it.

When I was a child I was more or less brainwashed into telling the psychologist that there was nothing wrong at home. When I was asked if my parents slapped me and I would say 'Sometimes,' he would ask 'Why did they do that?' and I would reply 'Because I'm naughty.' He would then ask why I was naughty and I couldn't explain it. In those days I suppose it was more acceptable to slap children.

I think I only saw the psychologist for about a year and my mother always came with me. I am sure that she would insist that there was nothing wrong at home. I think she still denies that there was ever a problem. At the time, she just became obsessed with stopping my father drinking.

I think it is all too painful for her to face up to now. She would rather not think about it at all. Even now I don't think she has any idea of psychological and emotional needs. She can't understand why I can't cope with certain aspects of life. Nor does she see why I am the way I am. I haven't got anything to say to her any more, really.

I am not very close to anyone in my family. There is poor communication in the family all round. It is something I have tried very consciously not to re-create and the thought of having children of my own terrifies me.

Eventually, when my father became consistently violent with my mother, she started leaving him. I was in my early teens then. But he would always get her back. He would behave himself for a couple of weeks and then he would get bad again. It went on like that for about six years. During those years, he picked on me more and more. Sometimes when she left I would go and live with her.

No one comes out and says that stammering can sometimes be a consequence of emotional and physical abuse. Very little is said about it. Yet I feel that in my case it was probably a contributing factor. I think I stammer because I grew up with so much fear as a child.

In addition to my father's violence, there was something else going on during the time that I was about nine or ten years old that used to terrify me. There was a boy down the road who used to set his dog on me. I was afraid of dogs and he must have known that. This was all happening about the same time.

I certainly can't say I had a happy childhood. I'm glad it's over.

I remember when I was about 17 years old I went to see the doctor to get help for my stammer. I was starting to have to go for interviews for jobs. I asked for speech therapy but he just fobbed me off with tranquillisers. He told me to take them as they would make me feel more confident. They didn't do anything for me at all. I was left with the feeling that nothing could be done about it.

It wasn't until about five years ago that I found out about The British Stammering Association and I joined. I've been very surprised by it. Meeting other stammerers has made me feel more 'normal' and not so isolated because of the way I speak.

I have done a couple of speech therapy courses which have made me *feel more confident, and I don't feel as bad about my speech as I did at one time. Part of me feels quite stupid when I stammer. It has made me very shy. I think it has kept me quiet. I don't feel as if I am a spontaneous speaker. I feel I have to think about everything before I say it. I don't feel very spontaneous at all when I talk.*

I think I have quite a few emotional problems apart from my stammer. I have problems relating to men, which is not surprising, I suppose.

I have had psychotherapy on and off over the years, but I know I have still got a long way to go. Fluency of speech comes and goes depending on how I am feeling about myself. If I'm feeling rotten about myself my speech is bad and vice versa.

SELF-HELP TECHNIQUES

In previous chapters we have looked at different ways in which you can obtain help for your stammer. You can go to a speech and language therapist. You can attend intensive courses, some of which are residential while others are not. You can focus on the emotional and psychological aspects of stammering. You can consider some of the personal growth therapies on offer or try one of the complementary therapies that are described briefly in Chapter Eleven. You may want to work on the physical and emotional aspects of stammering at the same time and there is no reason at all why you should not do this.

However, you may prefer to tackle the problem on your own. If you are prepared to put in the time and keep up the motivation, there is no reason why you cannot help yourself in the comfort of your own home. Two main approaches you can use are block modification and slow prolonged speech. Both these techniques can be used when speaking on the telephone, something which most people who stammer find difficult.

· *Block Modification* ·

This a popular approach to therapy used in this country. It is based mainly on the work of Charles Van Riper, a famous American speech therapist who stammered himself. He believed it was helpful to accept your stammering and learn to stammer in an easier manner with less tension and struggle. This approach has become known as 'Stammer more fluently', as opposed to the slow prolonged speech approach of 'Speak more fluently'.

Van Riper defined four phases in his approach to therapy:

● finding out what you do when you stammer (*identification*)
● reducing your negative feelings about stammering (*desensitisation*)
● changing how you stammer (*modification*)
● maintaining the progress you have made (*stabilisation*).

The modification phase is perhaps the most important because this is where you actually change your stammer, or 'block', as Van Riper calls it. Before you can successfully do this you have to know how you stammer and you need to feel less emotional about it.

· *Identification* ·

As with anything else, the first thing you have to do is to define the problem. How do you stammer, and when? What or who triggers it?

One of the most difficult aspects of any condition is to accept that you have it. If you don't really have it or if it doesn't really bother you, you don't have to confront it. I myself had migraines for 10 years before I acknowledged that it was migraine I was suffering from. The first step for me was to define the pattern of my migraines. So let's start this chapter on self-help by enabling you to define your stammer.

Here are some questions to ask yourself.

- Do you repeat sounds ('s-s-s-supper') or syllables ('sup-sup-sup-supper')?
- Do you prolong sounds ('sssssssupper')?
- Do you get blocked in speech so that you are unable to make any sound ('... supper')?
- Do you close your eyes or rush through speech?
- Do you try to avoid the word by changing it for another that is easier to say?
- Do you give up speaking altogether?
- Do you think your stammer is severe or quite mild?
- Do you think that it is holding you back in your social life or at work?
- Is it better with some people and in some situations than others?
- How do you feel when you stammer? Embarrassed? Annoyed? Frustrated?
- Do you get angry at other people, at yourself, or both?

· *Desensitisation* ·

Answering these kinds of question should start enabling you to see the pattern of your stammer and give you a clearer picture of how it affects you. You will not be able to modify your stammering unless you reduce your sensitivity to it. This can be achieved by talking openly about it, maintaining eye contact, reducing your avoidance of stammering and stammering voluntarily.

Talking openly

Talking to one or two selected people about your stammer can help you to deal with it more openly. Talking to people you like and feel close to may make you feel less anxious about stammering. You may find that people are no where near as critical or bothered about stammering as you believe them to be. In all probability your friends will just accept it as part of you and those you have confided in may well go out of their way to help you be more open about it.

Maintaining eye contact

It is very natural when you are embarrassed to look away or look down at your feet. If you are stammering and you feel shy or awkward about it, you may not want to see the face of the people you are trying to talk to, their uneasy expressions. In Chapter Seven Nav describes an interview he had when he applied to go to medical school: 'My eye contact was non-existent. I did not want to look at the panel because it would have intensified the embarrassment and the pain. . . . At one stage when I did look at the people on the panel I saw that they were looking down at the table.' Many people will empathise with Nav's experience.

Maintaining eye contact will not stop you from stammering, but it may reduce the embarrassment all round. It can put your listener much more at ease. If, while your mouth is struggling to produce the words, your eyes are expressing friendly messages, the listener will pick up on those messages and wait calmly for you to finish. He or she will not be worried or embarrassed about your stammering because you have conveyed that it is OK. It isn't bothering you. Never underestimate the power of non-verbal communication.

The eye contact should be soft, warm and friendly. Glaring would be counter-productive. This may sound obvious, but it is very difficult when you are in turmoil inside to appear gentle and friendly on the outside. You may naturally glare in this situation, because you are annoyed not with your listener, but with yourself. Maintaining the right eye contact is a skill that will need to be practised.

Sit or stand in front of a mirror and let out your stammer. Look at your eyes and practise producing a soft expression. When you feel you have made some progress, try it while talking to someone on the phone. Put a mirror next to the phone and watch yourself while you are talking and, possibly, genuinely stammering. Keep practising until it feels comfortable.

The next step is to test it in the outside world, on a face-to-face basis. Don't try and maintain soft eye contact all the time to start off with. Practise during conversations with a friend or a sympathetic colleague. Tell them beforehand about what you are going to do. As soft eye contact begins to feel more natural, you will be able to use it more frequently. Eventually, you will be able to maintain it, hopefully, most of the time.

Reducing avoidance

One of the most positive steps you can take to deal with stammering is to cut down on your avoidance tactics. It is also probably the most difficult. If you have stammered all your life, avoiding certain words and situations will probably have become second nature to you. This may have enabled you to stammer less and made your life easier in the short term, but in the long term it has helped to keep the stammer in place.

You still fear the same situations, perhaps even more than when you were younger. You will hardly have spoken some of the words you are afraid of, maybe not for years. Some of these words may be significant ones; your name, for example. Nav in Chapter Seven comments that even a two-year-old can say his own name, but he couldn't, so what chance did he have of getting a job? In Chapter Twelve Bob tells the story of a telephone conversation in which he infuriated the person on the other end by resolutely avoiding telling him his name.

In his book *Self-therapy for the Stutterer*, published by the Stuttering Foundation of America and available from the BSA, Malcolm Fraser makes this point:

> While temporarily affording relief, avoidances will actually increase your fears and cause you more trouble in the long run .... Stuttering will be perpetuated by successful avoidances.

He goes on to list some avoidance tactics, such as not speaking on the phone and avoiding speaking situations or social contacts. Other ruses include talking more quickly, in a monotone or a singsong voice, acting like a clown and pretending to be hard of hearing. He continues:

> Postponements include various stalling devices such as clearing the throat, swallowing, coughing, blowing the nose, putting in

unnecessary words such as 'you know' or 'I mean', or 'that is' or making excessive use of interjections like 'uh', 'er', 'well', waiting for someone to supply the word, etc. Substitutions involve using synonyms, easy words or other phrases for those on which you think you might block . . . . Postponements and substitutions are variations of avoidance practices.

How do you change the habit of a lifetime? First, become aware of your avoidance tactics. Armed with your diary or a pocket notebook, spend the next week or so watching yourself and listening to what you say. What words do you avoid or substitute? Are there situations, like answering the phone or asking for things in a shop, that you do not do if you can possibly help it? Jot it all down and at the end of the week take a look at the notes you have made.

One thing is certain: you are not going to stop all the avoidances at once. Choose the one you would feel most comfortable about changing or, better still, the one you would be happiest to eliminate. This may be always limiting yourself to picking things off a shelf in shops instead of asking for what you want. Perhaps it is refusing to speak on the telephone, or substituting certain words. Choose one thing and work on that.

If, for instance, you decide that you want to be able to ask for goods in shops, pick just one item to start off with. Practise saying the word at home and then try it for real. When you have accomplished that, try asking for two things next time, and so on. If you would like to stop avoiding feared words, tackle them one at a time. Make a point of saying the word and not the one that you normally use as a substitute. Work on all the problem words on your list one by one until they become an established part of your vocabulary.

Voluntary stammering

You can usually get some relief from your fear and tension by stammering voluntarily. If you can stammer on purpose, you are in control and this should reduce your tension. Voluntary stammering should take the form of simple repetitions or short prolongations of the first sound or syllable of a word, or the word itself. It should be done only with non-feared words, and in a calm and relaxed manner.

Voluntary stammering can help eliminate some of your shame and embarrassment. The more you practise, the easier it will become. A good goal to aim for is being willing to stammer without being emotionally involved.

· *Modification* ·

There are three types of modification you can use to improve your fluency:

- *Cancellation* – you go back and correct your stammer after you have stammered. This can be very helpful and should be practised first.
- *Pull-out* – you correct your stammer while you are in the middle of stammering.
- *Pre-block* – you prepare to move smoothly through a stammer which you can anticipate. This is the final objective of the approach.

Cancellations

Here is the sequence of actions you should follow when you do a cancellation:

- First, finish saying the word on which you have stammered, then come to a complete stop and pause.
- Now try to relax the tension you can feel in your speech and ask yourself how you got stuck on the word.
- Review what you can do to change and improve the sound of the word and mentally rehearse this.
- Now repeat the word in the new way in a smooth prolonged manner.

Although this may seem a long and involved process, it should only take a few seconds and it will get quicker with practice. Try not to be embarrassed when you deliberately stammer repeatedly. It will show other people that you are working on your difficulties. Most people are considerate and will respect you for your efforts.

Pull-outs

In a pull-out, you change your stammer while you are in the middle of it. When you find yourself stammering, don't pause or stop and try again. Instead, continue stammering, but smoothly slow it down. Keep your stammer going until you feel that you are in control of it. Then figure out an easier way to carry on and put this new approach into effect.

Pre-blocks

In the last stage, the pre-block modification, you prepare to overcome your stammering before it happens. When you anticipate stammering on a word, pause just before saying the word in order to plan how to approach it. Don't speak until you have worked out how you usually stammer on the sound and what you can now do to improve your fluency.

People who stammer often have problems with making the transition from a hard consonant sound to the softer vowel sound which follows. The slow prolonged manner of keeping the sounds flowing as you say the feared word, is designed to make this transition smooth. Do not be embarrassed by the pause or the slowed speech. You will find the pause becoming shorter and shorter as you become better at dealing with your stammering in this way.

If you can move smoothly through your anticipated stammering you will be well on your way to more fluent speech. It will also give you the good feeling of knowing that your stammering is under control.

· *Stabilisation* ·

Even if you have made rapid progress using block modification, be a little cautious. Strange as it may seem, you may need to adjust to your improved fluency. Since you may not have been used to speaking freely, any inability to express yourself may result in a loss of confidence in the approach you are using.

Sadly, stammering can sometimes recur. You will need to guard against slipping back into old habits. Your old fears may come back too. If they do, remember that a willingness to stammer in a modified way can be an important factor in improving your fluency.

As time passes, you should continue to gain confidence in your ability to control your speech. Be assertive. The more confidence you have, the more freedom from fear you will experience. On the other hand, don't expect too much. Don't be anxious to talk too well too soon and try not to make excessive demands on your speech. Also it is important to remind yourself that, just because you speak more fluently, you will not automatically have more friends or get a better job, although, in time, this may well happen!

· *Slow Prolonged Speech* ·

This is a technique for slowing down your speech and talking in a much smoother, more prolonged way. You learn to take time to slide softly into the words one after another. It helps you to control your speech so that you stammer very much less. Speaking really slowly minimises the likelihood of stammering. Of course, when you speak extremely slowly you won't sound the same as everyone else, but it is not suggested that you speak like that all the time. The object is to correct some of your speech problems by, first of all, slowing down your speech while you are getting to grips with the techniques involved, and then building up speed until you are speaking at a much more normal rate, but with much less stammering. Practise talking at the slow speed at home. You are not expected to do it in the course of your daily life.

The British Stammering Association has a cassette designed to teach slow prolonged speech (available from their head office) which makes it much easier to acquire this skill. The cassette details the technique, takes you through the different speeds of speech and explains what to do as you go along. It is very modestly priced. The description given here is very brief; it is intended mainly as a taster.

Bear in mind that this is not a technique that you will be able to learn overnight. It will take a lot of practice and perseverance. It is not recommended for children under the age of 12.

Pausing and breathing

In addition to speaking slowly, it is important to learn to pause frequently. Many stammerers don't do this, sometimes because they are anxious to get to the end of the sentence and sometimes because they are worried that if they do pause, they will not be able to get started again.

Everybody has to pause in speech to draw breath. If you run out of breath, you cannot control your speech and it is very difficult, if not impossible, to speak fluently. Have you ever had a conversation with someone who was out of breath, from hurrying or running? If you have, you may remember that it was hard to understand him or her; it may have been almost as uncomfortable for you to listen as it was for them to speak.

Learning to pause before you run out of breath is vital. If someone chips in and interrupts while you pause, so be it. Once you have mastered the technique, you won't worry so much about being unable to start again. Pausing also gives you time to think about what you are going to say, which is an important way of controlling your speech.

You will be practising speaking at different speeds, starting at 40 words per minute (wpm) and working up to 110 wpm. At the slowest speed, you will have plenty of time to fit in your pauses, breathe in a relaxed way, slide into the words one after another and get the feeling of being in control.

Soft contacts

When you slow down your speaking, you can practise other parts of speech that you may find difficult. Many stammerers experience problems when two of the speech organs (lips, tongue, roof of the mouth and teeth) make contact. For instance, to make a T or a D sound the tip of the tongue touches the roof of the mouth. To sound a B or a P the lips touch. An F or V sound requires the bottom lip to touch the upper teeth.

The P and B sounds (known as plosives) are made by closing the lips and building up the pressure of air in the mouth. The lips are then separated and the air released. What can happen in stammering is that the contact between the lips is tense and hard. The air pressure in the mouth builds up and the words are forced out. Sometimes it takes a while for the word to come out, resulting in a silent block. The pressure is building up in the mouth and the person is becoming extremely anxious and tense. Stammerers often remark how tense the upper part of their body becomes when they are stammering severely.

The idea is to learn to make these plosive sounds lightly and softly, so that the words come out gently. Try to practise making these sounds very lightly. It may help you to sit in front of a mirror and watch your mouth as you practise.

Prolonging

Learning to prolong or stretch the sounds, particularly the vowels, while you move from word to word is also part of the technique. It can be quite difficult to master this which is one of the reasons for slowing down the rate of speech. It enables you to practise. Once you are more used to sliding into the words, you will be able to forget about prolonging the vowels.

Equipment

You don't need a great deal of equipment. A tape recorder, blank cassettes and a stop-watch or watch with a seconds hand are basically all that is required. Make sure that it is a tape recorder that you can speak into. A Walkman may not be suitable, but you can pick up hand-held tape recorders that are not very expensive. You will also need to find newspapers, magazines or books to read from.

You may want to sit in front of a mirror to watch your mouth as you are learning to make the soft contact and prolonging sounds, but you don't have to. It's best to do whatever you are comfortable with. As well as reading from texts, practise talking to yourself at the different speeds described.

Speaking at different rates

Allow yourself up to 20 minutes twice a day to practise. Take a passage of text from any reading material of your choice and mark off a passage of 40 words. Give yourself one minute to read it (i.e. you will be reading at a speed of approximately 40 wpm). It may take you a little time to get the speed right – you will probably find it unbelievably slow – but if you time yourself, it will soon get easier.

At this speed you should be able to practise making the plosive sounds lightly and softly. You can try stretching and drawing out the vowels and perhaps the consonants as well. You can practise pausing and breathing and giving yourself plenty of time to breathe and slide from one word into the next. If the text is too long, don't worry, just start by reading two sentences and then add more as your confidence grows.

Mark off a few more 40-word passages so that you have a choice of material to practise on. Remember to record yourself. It might be worth keeping some of these early recordings to remind yourself how you got on when you first started. Later on, if you feel you are not progressing quickly enough, you can play back the early tapes. You will probably be pleasantly surprised.

Keep reading at 40 wpm until you feel comfortable with the techniques you are practising. You may find that you are speaking without stammering at this very slow rate. You may like to practise it on other people, but don't do it out of the blue; they may be disconcerted. If you have a friend or relative who would be supportive, enlist their help. Tell them what you are practising and introduce the technique occasionally when you are speaking to them. Do not try to speak like this all the time, just use it two or three times during the course of a conversation.

When you feel that you can move on, find passages of 60 words. Again, allow yourself one minute to read each one. This is a good speed for practising, because you can still use the techniques of light contact, pausing, prolonging the sounds and sliding from word to word, but now your speech will sound more animated. It is slower than normal speech, but remember, you are only beginning to experience speaking without stammering. Practise until you are confident at this speed. If you start stammering, go back to the 40 wpm for a little while before returning to 60 wpm. Try not to get despondent if this happens; it can take several months to master this technique.

By the time you are reaching for the newspaper or magazine to mark out 80-wpm texts, your speech should have become smoother and gentler at the lower speeds. At this new speed you will be working on ensuring that you do not allow the tension to come back. You will be speaking faster, almost at a normal pace, but at the same time concentrating on keeping your breathing relaxed and making sure that you pause frequently. Keeping the plosive sounds light and soft will also be very important. However, you will find that at this rate of speaking you will not be prolonging or stretching the sounds as you did before.

Eighty wpm is a very good speed to practise at, because it is not very much slower than the normal rate. If you get used to speaking without stammering at this speed, you can use it if and when you get into trouble in the outside world. If you find you start to stammer when you are talking in a difficult situation, just bring your speech down to the level of 80 wpm and you may well find that it relaxes you and puts you back in control.

The average speaking rate is around 110–140 wpm, so when you start practising at 110 wpm, you are speaking on the slow side of normal. You really don't need to talk any faster than this. Needless to say, at this speed it can be quite difficult to maintain all the parts of the technique you have learned. Allow yourself frequent pauses to make sure you have plenty of breath and time to think about what you are going to say. You will still need to concentrate on making the contacts sounds light and soft so that you slide into the words instead of pushing them out.

If, while you are practising the technique, you ever find yourself stammering, go back to a slower rate until you have mastered it.

· *Speaking on the Telephone* ·

Many people, including non-stammerers, avoid using the telephone. Collecting your thoughts and trying to express them coherently to someone you can't see can be unnerving, even if you do not have a speech difficulty. However, you can look at this in another way: if you cannot see the other person, you cannot be put off by them. You won't see if they pull a face or look at you strangely.

It can be helpful to put a mirror by the telephone and watch yourself speaking on the phone. Observe what happens when you stammer; notice where the tension is in your face and other parts of your body. This will clarify your picture of your stammering.

An important aim is to be willing and able to make phone calls and answer them without worrying. According to The British Stammering Association, making a telephone call can be split into three phases: preparation, the call and assessment.

Preparing the call

The best way to confront any situation that causes anxiety, such as making a speech, sitting an exam or undertaking a difficult journey is to prepare for it. Do not simply pick up the phone and hope that the right words will come into your head. Have a piece of paper in front of you. Write down the name of the person you are telephoning and list all the points you want to make. You can then go through them, even if you are interrupted or distracted.

If it is an important or difficult call you have to make and you are particularly nervous about it, try phoning a friend or someone you are used to first, have a quick chat to relax you and then ease into the more stressful call. You may find it much easier than you imagined. If you have a number of calls to make, list them in order of horrors. Put the ones you fear the least at the top and work your way down to the worst ones. By the time you have reached the main one, you will have got into the swing of phoning.

However, the big caveat to this is: don't put off making that call. Keep an eye on the time and, if necessary, skip some of the easier calls and move on to the ones you fear. The more you put off making phone calls you are anxious about, the more difficult it becomes. Ease yourself into the task with the more straightforward calls, but never lose sight of your target: the call you're afraid to make.

The call

If you start to stammer, try not to hide it. Stammer openly, gently and easily. Try not to force out the words, and slow down your speech. Don't worry if there is a silence, just concentrate on what you have to say.

Remember that your purpose is to communicate. Try to focus on the parts of your speech that are fluent. Many stammerers forget about the times that they speak fluently and dwell on their stammer.

If you have made a call well, especially if it was a difficult one, congratulate yourself and give yourself a treat. Savour the good feeling the success has given you and remind yourself of it from time to time.

Many stammerers talk about having good and bad periods of fluency. If you are going through a more fluent and confident period, build on it. Make telephone calls, particularly local ones, even if they are not strictly necessary. Take advantage of the good times to build your confidence and confront your fears.

The assessment

Even people who do not stammer make phone calls that they feel were less than satisfactory. It is not difficult to get the impression that the person on the other end has not been listening or that you have failed to get your message across.

If you stammered very badly and it was a stressful call, do your best to forget about it and chalk it up to experience. Again, make an easy call if you can. Replace the bad experience with a good one. Tell yourself that there will be other phone conversations in which you will stammer less. It is not a disaster, just a phone call.

Receiving calls

Many people who stammer prefer to make phone calls rather than receive them. If you make the call you can do it in your own time and you can prepare for it. The random element of receiving telephone calls is what stammerers tend to dislike. It may feel out of control, but it need not be.

Don't rush to answer the phone. Take your time. Don't worry if there is someone within earshot who may see you block or hear you stammer. Try to keep them out of your mind and focus solely on the call. Don't be afraid of the initial silence on the phone if you struggle to say your first word. This is not all that unusual. People often pick up the phone and say nothing while they settle themselves down, shuffle through papers or finish a conversation with a colleague; maybe they picked up the phone on someone else's behalf and are waiting for them to return. Also, bear in mind that there is likely to be some background noise which will reassure the caller that he or she has not been cut off.

The main thing to learn about telephone technique, whether you are making the call or receiving it, is that practice makes it very much easier. The more you do it, the less you will fear it. The less you fear it, the better you will be at talking on the phone. Here are some general pointers:

- Confront your fear of the phone. Talk about what you find difficult and how you can overcome it.
- Become aware of the situations in which you avoid using the telephone and carefully tackle each of these calls in turn.
- Make phone calls instead of writing letters whenever you can.
- For a while, try to take responsibility for answering the phone at home, rather than deliberately walking past it.
- Watch and listen to non-stammerers using the phone. You may find that they are nowhere near as fluent as you believed them to be. You may be quite amazed at the hesitation and the umming and ahhing that goes on in most conversations.
- Talk about your stammer. This may be difficult at first, particularly if you have avoided the subject for most of your life, but try. Many stammerers say that talking about stammering has reduced their anxiety about it. If people know that you stammer, they will expect silences and stammering on the phone.
- You may find it useful to tape-record the telephone calls you make at home. Note your speech and the speed at which you speak. If there is any stammering notice what caused or preceded this. Try to learn from each recording and improve on your technique during the next call. If you do this over a period of time you may be able to identify some of your recurring problems and troublesome words.

Take your time

With all of these self-help ideas, the key is to take it a bit at a time. All the suggestions look fairly easy on paper, but they can be difficult to put into practice. You need to persevere.

Try not to become angry with yourself if and when you fail to achieve the goals you have set yourself. Give yourself treats and praise when you have made an improvement. Remind yourself that it was not easy, but you managed it. Remember also that it is virtually impossible to keep improving. No matter what we are learning, progress is often followed by periods when we stand still or even take a step backwards. This is natural, so try not to be dispirited when it happens.

· *Self-help Groups* ·

There are a number of self-help groups for stammerers up and down the country. Although each is independent, they are encouraged by The British Stammering Association. Many also liaise with each other.

They aim to provide a place where stammerers and others interested in the issues of stammering – partners, friends and therapists, for example – can meet, talk freely, exchange ideas and offer support. Apart from the obvious social benefits, these groups provide an ideal opportunity for people to practise speech techniques they may be apprehensive about trying out elsewhere. Some of the groups are attended by speech therapists who can give help and advice. Other types of therapy may also be discussed. Many groups run workshops for their members from time to time.

Bob Adams, who started the Stammerers' Self-help Group in Doncaster, explains what happens there:

We meet every two weeks for two hours or sometimes longer. We get people attending from all over the area. Some people travel for 40 miles to get to us. The hardest part is to come through the door for the first time. After that people usually come back again and again. It took one of our members, who had been advised by his speech therapists to come, over six months to actually pluck up the courage to attend a meeting. Now he hardly misses a single meeting.

In a typical evening we will all sit around and take a couple of minutes each to talk about how we have been in the last two weeks. We talk mainly about how we've coped with our speech and if there are any new members, we will give them a brief run-down on our personal history as regards stammering. It lets them know more about us. Also relaxation is very important and we've found that simple relaxation and breathing exercises are well worth doing at the start of a meeting.

There may also be some committee-type work where we give an update of anything we've been involved in that the other members of the group might not be aware of. Then there is usually an activity of some sort. For instance, recently we have been doing some 'speaking circle' work. It is an American idea called 'transformational speaking'. It is a powerful way of talking which involves pauses and maintaining soft eye contact at all times. It is not aimed solely at stammerers but at all kinds of people, including salespeople, teachers and therapists.

If we are doing this particular exercise, we will remove our chairs from the friendly circle we normally sit in and put them in rows, so as to be more formal. Each person will take it in turn to go out in front of the others and talk for three minutes. People can always opt out of these exercises if they don't want to do them, but they are encouraged to take part and it is a safe, non-judgemental environment.

The first thing to do is to make soft eye contact for a few seconds with each member of the group. You don't have to speak at all. If you then want to speak, you can do, but the idea is not to have prepared what you want to say. You are encouraged to speak spontaneously. If you go blank and forget what you want to say, that's fine, but you have to maintain soft eye contact. It's known as 'staying in the void'. The group has to maintain full concentration on the person who is out in front.

We've tried this a few times in Doncaster and we've really started getting into it and are finding it very powerful. It's a very effective way of communicating. People realise that they don't have to fill every second with speech. In fact, it's far more effective if they allow pauses to occur naturally. Maintaining soft eye contact keeps the connection between speaker and listener alive.

From the moment we walk through the door the idea is to be focused on speech. This may be just having a chat with someone else, or it may be that some people want to practise a particular technique. Someone may say that he or she is trying slow pro-longed speech or block modification and wants to monitor how they are doing. That can be very helpful.

We have two local speech and language therapists who attend the group as well as student therapists who join us. Sometimes we do workshops. We've recently done some on assertiveness training. It's not only stammerers who come. Often partners attend as well. This helps them to understand a lot more about problems which, although linked to stammering, are not as apparent as the overt speaking dysfluency.

We also arrange social activities. We will go out for a meal or a drink or, occasionally, a show. We have forged links with many other self-help groups, including the Leeds, Sheffield and Barnsley groups. We send out a monthly newsletter to stammerers, therapists and other interested parties throughout the United Kingdom and mainland Europe. The newsletters are well received and the feedback is very positive.

If you would like to find out whether there is a self-help group for stammerers in your area, contact The British Stammering Association.

· *Richard* ·

Most of Richard's life has been affected by his stammer. His early attempts to learn speech techniques were not very productive. He became more successful later in his life by accepting his stammer and attending many different self-help groups .

I have had a stammer most of my life, and most of my life has been affected by my stammer. My mother told me that it only became noticeable when I was about 11 years old, but I think that avoidance had been the name of the game until then as I can't remember not stammering.

I found school a bit of a war zone; the main obstacle of every day was how to acknowledge my name at register time. Buses and trains were no better; I rarely got a ticket to where I wanted; it could be one mile either way, dependent on the stop I felt confident in asking for, but I got by. Being only of average intelligence, I suppose the first part of my speaking life – speaking was always at the front of my mind – was mainly avoidance. It wasn't that easy at home, not that I had a bad upbringing, but being in a family of seven and being the only one stammering, I found it hard to join in around the table.

I remember reading a Sarah Doudney poem called 'The Water Mill' in which the recurring line is 'The mill will never grind with the water that has passed.' I don't know if it was my early learning of life or something instinctive in my genes but I have always managed, so far, to look forward and not ponder on the pitfalls of the past and I think it's something worth passing on to anyone reading this.

Throughout my life, once every five years or so, I have sought and obtained speech therapy. In the early school years, I didn't find therapy very constructive. 'What you are doing when you speak is that you are breathing in through your vocal box, and not out like your fluent friends do.'

My parents paid for my next therapy. It was at the Grosvenor Hotel, Deansgate, Manchester. The technique this gentleman taught was to talk with 'a-s-l-o-w-s-t-a-r-t-and-then-jointhewordstogetherdeadnatural-like'. One technique I never forgot, and it has helped me through the years, was how to reply when purchasing something in a shop, having stated clearly what you want, only to be answered 'Pardon?' He taught us that, instead of regressing five years, you should restate your purchase in 'as many decibels as you can muster!' Another good thing he did, before he left to go to another town, was to get everyone present to form a self-help group where we met once a fortnight for the next six months.

This was my first experience of attending many self-help groups of one form or another, and I'm still going to them.

There were years on my own, though, trying to help myself, clutching at one technique or other. These I found hard and unprofitable, sending me down dead ends or coming out speaking like a dalek. But having gone to all kinds of speech therapy of one sort of another, where it was mainly slowed speech technique, describing picture-postcards, word games, mock phone calls and so on, I can say that therapy in the past 10 to 15 years has improved tremendously and is now both helpful and instructive and on the NHS.

About 12 years ago one therapist's first observation was: 'You don't accept your stammer, do you?' When I thought about it, no I didn't. The therapist then got me to make a list of people to admit my stammer to, from the easiest to the hardest. I had to put in false stammers which, although very hard at first, does desensitise the situation. Eye contact was the next task. I still have to make a conscious effort to do this, but for me it works like magic on occasions. The therapist suggested I join the BSA. Through it I have made friends with other stammerers, gone to open days and workshop weekends where I have learnt a variety of techniques and acquired new information. With their help, we (notice the 'we' nowadays) have been able to run a self-help group in our local area. Because of modern therapy, The British Stammering Association, and self-help groups, I am stammering more and more easily. We stammerers have to help ourselves, but there is a lot of help out there – and it's global.

11

COMPLEMENTARY THERAPIES

Complementary therapies, with their holistic approach, can be very attractive to people looking for ways to deal with any disorder. For people who stammer, hypnotherapy is one that is often tried, with varying degrees of success. Reflexology, meditation and yoga are unlikely to help speech directly, but practising them can bring about a feeling of calm and relaxation which can be extremely helpful.

The addresses of the relevant professional bodies appears in Useful Addresses at the end of the book.

· *Hypnotherapy* ·

In this treatment, the aim is to shift the patient's attention from external to internal awareness. Much of the work goes on in the patient's subconscious mind. The hypnotherapist will probably want to assess, as far as possible, the underlying cause of the problem as well as the maintaining factors. This may entail finding out about the person's life-style and investigating sources of stress and any other factors that may be triggering the condition, keeping it in place or making it worse. A medical history is usually taken. Attempts should also be made to ensure that hypnosis is a suitable therapy for the client.

The client is put into a light trance. This is a naturally occurring state, similar to day-dreaming or the slowing down, drifting feeling before you drop off to sleep.

Hypnotherapists maintain that in the hypnotic state, people tend to be much more receptive to therapy in the form of suggestions and imagery. This, they say, is because the left side of the brain, which is in charge of analytical and logical thought, shuts off, allowing the therapist to communicate with the client's subconscious mind without the blocks and defences that are usually in place. Many people remember almost everything that has happened while they were in the trance state.

The hypnotherapist may then try to explore the underlying reasons that are causing or contributing to the condition. These could be feelings of stress and anxiety, poor self-image, lack of confidence and other negative thinking patterns.

Many therapists also employ visualisation techniques with their clients. For example, they may be asked to imagine they are lying in a boat and with each gentle sway of the boat they feel more relaxed. Or they may be asked to visualise a particularly peaceful place they know and imagine themselves there. People who are not good at creating visual imagery can use their other senses. They can imagine feeling the sun on their bodies, hearing the birds chirping, smelling sea breezes or the scent of flowers, for example.

This process can be emphasised by positive and soothing self-talk, where the client tells himself: 'I am feeling calm,' 'I am in control' or 'My body is feeling relaxed,' for instance.

The aim of the hypnotherapy is to make the person self-sufficient, so that he or she will not need to keep going to the therapist. Patients are taught self-hypnosis and shown how to include the appropriate imagery and phrase suggestions for themselves.

As far as stammering is concerned, this therapy can help some people tackle feared situations by means of desensitisation techniques. Some speech and language therapists are trained in hypnosis, so if you are interested in this therapy, it is worth finding out if there are any therapists in your area who can offer this service.

· *Reflexology* ·

Like other complementary therapies, reflexology aims to help the whole body function more efficiently. The process is based on applying pressure to minute points in the feet. Each zone of the foot corresponds to a different part of the body, including limbs as well as internal organs. Applying pressure to the soles of the feet is believed to have a beneficial effect on stress-related illnesses. It is thought that reflexology works by releasing endorphins (morphine-like chemicals) in the brain.

In addition, if the patient feels pain when the therapist massages a certain zone on the foot, this may reveal problems in the correlating part of the body. It is apparently a very relaxing and soothing treatment.

Joyce Preece is a reflexologist who is married to a stammerer. She says:

I genuinely think that reflexology helps stammerers. It can ease the tension in the throat, shoulders, lung and chest areas. When treating stammerers I pay more attention to the zones on the feet that relate to those parts of the body.

It can unblock and release the tension that stammerers tend to have. It can be very useful in calming people down prior to making a speech or attending an important meeting. It promotes a feeling of well-being which can make one feel more confident.

· *Meditation* ·

Several people who stammer have said that being calm and relaxed helps them speak more fluently. Certainly, many find that when they are in stressful situations, such as job interviews, their fluency deteriorates. Learning to meditate is for many people one of the best ways of learning to unwind and lower the stress factor. There are many different forms of meditation and which one you choose is entirely up to you.

Yoga meditation (see also page 148) is readily available and quite easy to learn. Most yoga teachers include it in their classes. Transcendental Meditation (see below) is also easy to learn, but the training is fairly expensive. There are books that detail meditation techniques and there are meditation tapes you can buy which give you an idea of what meditation feels like. However, there is no short cut to learning to achieve deep relaxation.

Different forms of meditation suit different people and it can often be a case of trial and error before you find one that suits you.

At the very least, meditation should enable you to feel relaxed and still while you are meditating. If you meditate regularly, you may find that at least some of this feeling of inner quiet stays with you during the course of the normal day.

Transcendental Meditation

Many people throughout the world practise Transcendental Meditation. The technique, founded by Maharishi Mahesh Yogi, is not difficult to master. In a one-to-one session you are given a special sound or phrase called a mantra. You shut your eyes, quieten your mind and focus on the mantra. This helps get rid of all the little thoughts that race across your mind. Eventually you let go of the mantra and achieve a deep sense of stillness and inner quiet. The meditation sessions last between 15 and 20 minutes, but the feeling of peace is maintained, to some extent, throughout the day. As you become a regular meditator – and you are supposed to practise twice a day – this inner peacefulness is constantly replenished and emphasised. It is as simple as that.

Learning the technique doesn't come cheap but it is a one-off payment that lasts for life. Subsequent check-ups, if you need them, are free. Transcendental Meditation is taught in a seven-stage course which you can cover in about a week.

· *Yoga* ·

Yoga is a system of mental, physical and spiritual development which originated in India three thousand years ago. The word 'yoga' comes from an Indian word meaning 'to unite' and the discipline is said to restore a healthier balance to body and mind, helping the person to cope better with the stresses and strains of everyday living.

In a yoga class you will probably start by learning a series of stretching exercises that enable the body to become more supple. These postures are not just physical exercises but a way of gaining greater control over body function. Yoga asanas (postures) gently stretch and contract every muscle in the body. Joints are encouraged to move more freely, which results in improved posture and, it is said, greater stamina and vitality.

The emphasis in yoga is very much on individual development. If one member of the class is exceptionally supple, this would be considered irrelevant to the others. Some yoga teachers ask their students to keep their eyes closed while doing the asanas in order to increase concentration and bring home the non-competitive nature of the exercise.

Breathing techniques may also be taught. Yogis have used breath-control techniques for centuries as a means of improving health and vitality. They say that these techniques, practised in the right way under the guidance of a good teacher, can improve respiration in general.

Most classes invariably finish with a period of relaxation, when students are taught how to direct the mind to different parts of the body and instruct them to relax. This is followed by a period of deep relaxation.

Meditation is an important adjunct to yoga teaching. Different methods are used to quieten or concentrate the mind so as to achieve an inner silence.

If you are interested in taking up yoga, it is advisable to go to a class given by a qualified teacher. Most of the postures take some time to learn and it is important to get them right. Group classes are not usually expensive and they can be quite social. The British Wheel of Yoga is a well-established organisation with qualified teachers who run classes throughout the UK.

12

THE BRITISH STAMMERING ASSOCIATION

At one BSA Open Day, a young woman took the microphone. It was an 'open mike', available to anyone who wanted to say something. Her words were jerky and her speech was punctuated with silent blocks, but her eyes shone as she told the audience, numbering about a hundred people, that she had never spoken in front of so many people before. The truth of the matter was, she said, that she had spent 20 or so years of her life hardly speaking at all. But she had recently had some therapy which had given her this new-found confidence.

The young woman spoke for no more than about two minutes and then a man, also in his twenties, took the mike. He too told the audience about the things he had been doing to overcome the problems associated with stammering. During the course of his speech he experienced a fairly long block which, in other circumstances, might have thrown him. But, apart from a few words of encouragement from his friends, no one said anything. Most of the audience maintained eye contact with the speaker until he resumed talking. When he had finished his speech he was enthusiastically applauded.

The Mistress of Ceremonies, who had a quite severe, repetitive stammer, then introduced a nurse. He spoke about his experiences of stammering in the workplace. When he applied for the job of nurse, he met with a lot of opposition, and it was suggested that he improve his stammer first.

The nurse went on to describe how, at the start of his first day at work, he had to sit in a group, introduce himself to colleagues and tell a small anecdote about himself. This was an introductory process for all new members of staff, but one he found particularly stressful. However, once he had accomplished this, he had felt more confident, he told the audience. Then he explained how much he needed to use speech during the course of his work and how having to speak had improved both his confidence and his fluency.

One difficulty that he had not envisaged, the nurse said, was in talking to elderly people who were sometimes hard of hearing. He often had to repeat himself. 'It was good practice,' he told the audience. 'It taught me to speak clearly and precisely.'

He added that his speech had improved in recent months for a variety of reasons, including increased self-confidence, his ability to do his job well, increased mental flexibility and the practice of some speech techniques. He said that he used to consider himself a stammerer who was occasionally fluent, but now he thought of himself more as a fluent person who occasionally stammered.

One by one other people came up and took centre stage. Some spoke very briefly, while others talked for much longer. All had something they wanted to share with their fellow stammerers, who comprised the major part of the audience.

Breaking the silence is the main focus of The British Stammering Association. It does this in a number of ways. It provides information on self-help groups and intensive courses and offers a free advice and counselling service to help people obtain specialised speech therapy.

Its magazine *Speaking Out*, which is issued free to members, contains news about the different therapies that are available and keeps readers up to date on current theories about the causes of stammering. It also includes articles by speech and language therapists and other interested professionals, personal accounts by stammerers, news of regional groups and book reviews.

The BSA spreads information about stammering to members and the world at large through the leaflets it produces and by keeping in constant touch with the media. It encourages research into the causes and treatment of stammering and advocates improved speech and language therapy services.

As well as supporting self-help groups, the BSA runs schemes for pen-pals, telephone links for adult stammerers and parents of stammering children and audiotape correspondence. It has a postal lending library of books, tapes and videos and also operates a mail-order service for books, tapes and videos that are not otherwise readily available. It organises Open Days, like the one described at the beginning of this chapter, in different parts of the UK.

The leading charity in Britain for people who stammer and their relatives and friends, the BSA was founded in 1978. It aims to help both adult and child stammerers to overcome the limitations and problems caused by stammering, so that they can feel confident in doing all the things that they want to do.

Although there are speech and language therapists and other professionals who are members of the BSA, policy decisions are made solely by stammerers and by parents acting on behalf of their stammering children.

The charity has received some grants from the Department of Health, but relies mainly on donations from individuals, charitable trusts and companies as well as members' subscriptions and mail-order sales.

The BSA liaises with national stuttering organisations in other countries in Europe and around the world. The address is in the Useful Addresses section at the end of this book.

· *Bob* ·

I stammered from the age of about four. I first became aware of it when I was in infant school and I was taken out to go for therapy. It made me self-conscious. It didn't do much for me at the time and it only lasted for a few months.

I never used to put my hand up in class, because I was scared of stammering. None of my teachers talked to me about it and I am sure that made me feel even worse, It wasn't talked about at home either.

I was very sporty as a child. I was in many teams, which I think helped improve my self-esteem. Even though I couldn't read out in class and would have blocks and go bright red, I was still captain of various teams. I am an outgoing kind of person, which is good, because otherwise it would have been even more traumatic. I do enjoy talking.

I remember that when we had to read out in class it was a nightmare. My whole world would be focused on trying to get the words out. There would be massive blocks when no sound would come out and I'd really be trying to force it out. Or there would be long repetitions. Sometimes when I got outside, my friends would ask me to read because they wanted to hear me stammer and I would read fluently. They were never sure if I really stammered or if I was just putting it on in class. I was the joker in the class.

Stammerers often find that if they put on an accent or put on a voice they can talk or read fluently. I used to do that. Throughout my life, until two years ago, I have changed words or the lead-in to a sentence. Sometimes the words I substituted would alter the meaning of what I wanted to say.

When I left grammar school I went to work for the Coal Board in an office-based job. There was quite a bit of phone work involved because I was in purchasing. I found it extremely stressful. It was an open-plan office and I was convinced that people nearby were listening to me talking and stammering on the phone. When you are announcing yourself on the phone you can't change words, so I stammered a lot.

I remember one situation where I had phoned up this chap and instead of saying my name, I said that I was phoning from the branch I was working in. He kept asking me my name and I kept avoiding giving it because I knew I would stammer on it. He got very uptight and angry with me.

Apart from some therapy I had at a very early age I had none at all until two years ago, after I joined The British Stammering Association. I started going to speech therapy locally and then I went to an intensive course at the City Lit in London.

Some of the things that we did on the City Lit course, like voluntary stammering and working on the iceberg, I had already done locally. It was very helpful to have already done some of that work because it eased me into the course at the City Lit. That course changed my life. Prior to that I could not talk about stammering. I couldn't even admit that I stammered. I hoped that, if I was seen going for speech therapy, people would think I was going for some other treatment, like physiotherapy for instance.

It was the first time that I had done group work, which I found very helpful. We looked at the stammering iceberg in much more detail and in more depth. I think since it was an intensive course and because it was in a group it was much more emotional.

I was staying with friends at the time and I started to talk to them about the iceberg and about stammering. I explained to them how I felt. This was the first time I had talked to friends about my stammer and I became very tense and emotional and I stopped talking about it. The next time I tried to talk about it, it was the same thing. I became very emotional. But after this occasion I felt as if a weight had been lifted off me. All these feelings I had bottled up for years somehow came to the surface; all the self-hatred and the anger and things like that.

I started to realise that these feelings had had an important control over me. I had had these hidden feelings of hating myself because of my stammering. Once they were open and exposed they went away. I could accept that I stammered. Now I can admit that I stammer but I also know that there is a lot more to me than that.

As far as I am concerned, I will stammer for the rest of my life but hopefully in an open and controlled way and, for most of the time, without feeling tense and uptight about it. In the past I used to close my eyes and look away. As long as I don't do that and keep good eye contact I think I can communicate as well, if not better, than quite a lot of people. Being able to talk about how I felt diffused a lot of the emotional part of stammering.

One of the things we worked on in the course was learning not to change words and avoid situations or words. Initially you start stammering more. You may not appear more fluent but you have changed from being a covert stammerer to a more open one. There are techniques, of course, that you can learn that can help reduce or control the amount of stammering.

When you become desensitised to stammering through exercises like voluntary stammering you don't feel so embarrassed or foolish about it and what can also happen is that you stammer less.

There have been some positive aspects to being a stammerer. I used to work out in a gym with a chap who I knew stammered. He had heard me stammer and I had heard him but in the eight years that we had known each other we had never said anything about it to each other. I suppose the feeling was that if we didn't talk about it, it didn't exist. Anyway, after I came back from the City Lit I wanted to do more group work and there was nothing available in the area. So I said to this chap in the gym that I wanted to start a self-help group locally. And that's what we did.

Through the group I've made some very good friends. I have met a wide range of very friendly people, stammerers, non-stammerers and therapists as well. I have taken part in workshops and got involved in a wide range of things that I wouldn't have had a chance to experience had I not been a stammerer.

In the course of trying to help myself I feel I have helped others as well – and that's nice.

I honestly think that if you are a stammerer, you should join The British Stammering Association, have speech therapy and join a self-help group if there is one nearby. I think it is important to take control of your life and start helping yourself.

USEFUL ADDRESSES

Please note that if you require information to be sent to you, most of the organisations listed request that you send them a stamped addressed envelope.

The British Stammering Association
(BSA)
15 Old Ford Road
London E2 9PJ
0181 983 1003/0181 981 8818
Fax: 0181 983 3591

Anti-Bullying Campaign
185 Tower Bridge Road
London SE1 2US
0171 378 1446

The Secretary
Association for Rational Emotive
Behaviour Therapy
1 Jenkinson Close
Newcastle-Under-Lyme
Staffordshire ST5 2JP

British Association for Counselling
(BAC)
1 Regent Place
Rugby
Warwickshire CV21 2PJ
01788 578328

British Association for the Person-
Centred Approach
BM BAPCA
London WC1N 3XX
(Has a list of qualified members)

British Association of
Psychotherapists
37 Mapesbury Road
London NW2 4HJ
0181 452 9823

British Confederation of
Psychotherapists
37a Mapesbury Road
London NW2 4HJ
0181 830 5173
(Has a nationwide list of psychoana-
lytic psychotherapists)

British School of Reflexology
92 Sheering Road
Old Harlow
Essex CM17 0JW
01279 429060

The British Wheel of Yoga
1 Hamilton Place
Boston Road
Sleaford
Lincs NG34 7ES
01529 306851

The City Literary Institute
Keeley House
Keeley Street
London WC2B 4BA
0171 430 0548

Institute for Complementary
Medicine
P.O. Box 194
London SE16 1QZ
0171 237 5165

Kidscape
152 Buckingham Palace Road
London SW1W 9TR
0171 730 3300

The Michael Palin Centre for
 Stammering Children
Finsbury Health Centre
Pine Street
London EC1R 0JH
0171 530 4238

The McGuire Institute
Dassenbos 40
NL-2134 RE Hoofddorp
Holland

National Register of Hypnotherapists
 and Psychotherapists
12 Cross Street
Nelson
Lancashire BB9 7EN
01282 699 378
(Has a nationwide register)

Personal Construct Psychology
The Sail Loft
Mulberry Quay
Falmouth
Cornwall TR11 3HD

Relate
Herbert Gray College
Little Church Street
Rugby
Warwickshire CV21 3AP
01788 573241

Royal College of Speech and
 Language Therapists
7 Bath Place
Rivington Street
London EC2A 3DR
0171 613 3855
Fax: 0171 613 3854
(Has a nationwide register)

Transcendental Meditation
Freepost
London SW1P 4YY
0800 269 303 (Freephone)

United Kingdom Council for
 Psychotherapy (UKCP)
167–169 Gt Portland Street
London W1N 5FP
0171 436 3002
(Has a hypnotherapy section)

Westminster Pastoral Foundation
(counselling and psychotherapy)
23 Kensington Square
London W8 5HN
0171 937 6956

Young Minds Trust
2nd Floor 102–108 Clerkenwell Road
London EC1M 5SA
0171 336 8445

ACKNOWLEDGEMENTS

I should like to thank Peter Cartwright, Director of The British Stammering Association, as well as Lisa Boardman, David Preece and Tim Shanks, also from the BSA, for the help they all gave me. I am very grateful to John Harrison of the National Stuttering Project in America for sharing some of his ideas on stammering.

Many thanks to speech and language therapists Willie Botterill, Carolyn Cheasman, Peggy Dalton, Rosemarie Hayhow and Louise Wright for giving me their time, patience and extremely valuable advice. I should also like to thank therapists Judy Cooper of the British Association of Psychotherapists and Professor Windy Dryden of the Association for Rational Emotive Behaviour Therapy for giving me the benefit of their expertise.

I am particularly indebted to Amanda Lewis for her help with some of the research, wordprocessing and proofreading.

Most of all I should like to thank all the people who stammer who took the time to explain to me how stammering has affected their lives. Some of these interviews were conducted on the telephone, a medium that some stammerers find so difficult to use, but they volunteered to do it none the less. I have nothing but the deepest respect for them all.

INDEX